CHEMISTRY 1050

LAB MANUAL

4TH EDITION

Bettelheim| Landesburg| Lograsso

Australia • Brazil • Japan • Korea • Mexico • Singapore • Spain • United Kingdom • United States

CENGAGE
Learning

Chemistry 1050: Lab Manual, 4th Edition
Bettelheim, Landesburg, Lograsso

Senior Manager, Student Engagement:
Linda deStefano
Janey Moeller

Manager, Student Engagement:
Julie Dierig

Marketing Manager:
Rachel Kloos

Manager, Production Editorial:
Kim Fry

Manager, Intellectual Property Project Manager:
Brian Methe

Senior Manager, Production and Manufacturing:
Donna M. Brown

Manager, Production:
Terri Daley

Compositor:
MPS LTD

For product information and technology assistance, contact us at
Cengage Learning Customer & Sales Support, 1-800-354-9706

For permission to use material from this text or product,
submit all requests online at **cengage.com/permissions**
Further permissions questions can be emailed to
permissionrequest@cengage.com

Compilation © 2014 Cengage Learning
ISBN-13: 978-1-305-03264-4
ISBN-10: 1-305-03264-0

WCN: 01-100-101

Cengage Learning

5191 Natorp Boulevard
Mason, Ohio 45040
USA

Cengage Learning is a leading provider of customized learning solutions with office locations around the globe, including Singapore, the United Kingdom, Australia, Mexico, Brazil, and Japan. Locate your local office at:
international.cengage.com/region.

Cengage Learning products are represented in Canada by Nelson Education, Ltd.

For your lifelong learning solutions, visit **custom.cengage.com.**

Visit our corporate website at **cengage.com.**

Printed in the United States of America

Contents

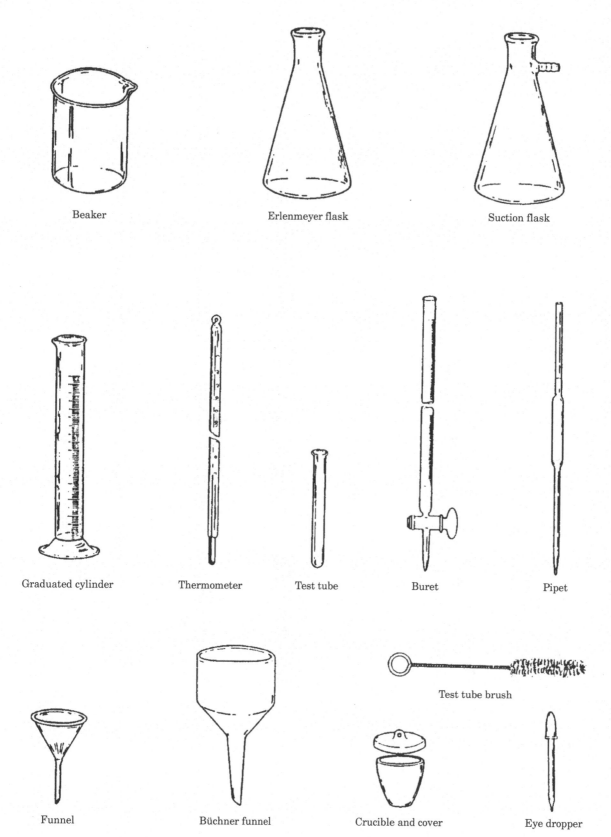

Beaker

Erlenmeyer flask

Suction flask

Graduated cylinder

Thermometer

Test tube

Buret

Pipet

Funnel

Büchner funnel

Test tube brush

Crucible and cover

Eye dropper

Figure 1
Common laboratory equipment.

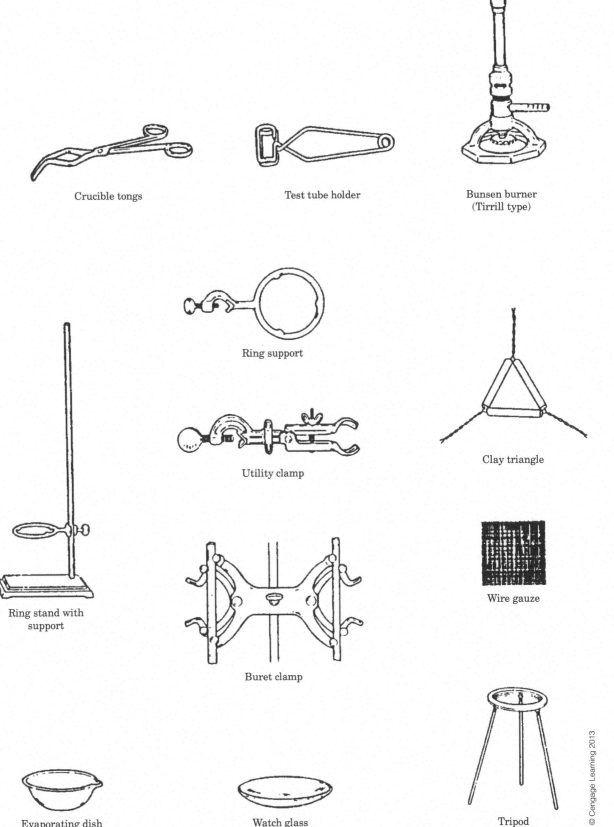

Crucible tongs

Test tube holder

Bunsen burner
(Tirrill type)

Ring support

Utility clamp

Clay triangle

Ring stand with
support

Buret clamp

Wire gauze

Evaporating dish

Watch glass

Tripod

Figure 1
Continued

Laboratory Techniques: Using the Laboratory Gas Burner; Making Laboratory Measurements

---

BACKGROUND

Using the Laboratory Gas Burner

Bunsen burners provide a ready source of heat in the chemistry laboratory. In general, because chemical reactions proceed faster at elevated temperatures, the use of heat enables the experimenter to accomplish many experiments more quickly than would be possible at room temperature. The burner illustrated in Figure 1.1 is typical of the burners used in most general chemistry laboratories.

A burner is designed to allow gas and air to mix in a controlled manner. The gas often used is "natural gas," mostly the highly flammable and odorless hydrocarbon methane, CH_4. When ignited, the flame's temperature can be adjusted by altering the various proportions of gas and air. The gas flow can be controlled either at the main gas valve or at the gas control valve at the base of the burner. Manipulation of the air vents at the bottom of the barrel allows air to enter and mix with the gas. The hottest flame has a nonluminous violet outer cone, a pale-blue middle cone, and a dark-blue inner cone; the air vents, in this case, are opened sufficiently to assure complete combustion of the gas. Combustion of the gas yields carbon dioxide and water.

$$CH_4(g) + 2O_2(g) \rightarrow CO_2(g) + 2H_2O(g)$$

Lack of air produces a cooler, luminous yellow flame. This flame lacks the inner cone, most likely is smoky, and often deposits soot on objects it contacts. The soot is due to small particles of carbon from unburned fuel, which luminesce and give the yellow flame. Too much air blows out the flame.

In the chemistry laboratory, much of the work that is carried out is with specialized glassware. It is important to understand the properties of the glass used in the makeup of this glassware and the limitations that these properties impose.

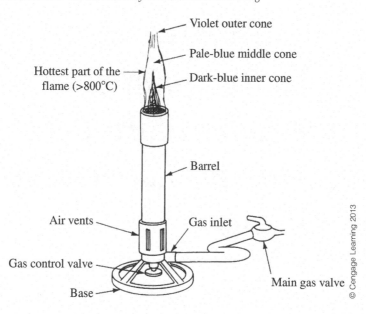

Figure 1.1
The Bunsen burner.

Glass is a super-cooled liquid. Unlike crystalline solids, which have sharp melting points, glass softens when heated and flows. However, not all glass is the same; there are different grades and compositions. Most laboratory glassware is made from borosilicate glass (containing silica and borax compounds). Commercially, this type of glass is known as *Pyrex*® (made by Corning Glass) or *Kimax*® (made by Kimble Glass). This glass does not soften very much below 800°C and is able to withstand most heating operations done in the laboratory. In addition, borosilicate glass has a low thermal coefficient of expansion. This refers to the material's change in volume per degree change in temperature. Borosilicate glass expands or contracts slowly when heated or cooled. Thus, glassware composed of this material can withstand rapid changes in temperature and can resist cracking.

Soft glass, on the other hand, is a poor material for laboratory glassware. Glass of this type is composed primarily of silica sand, SiO_2, and softens in the region of 300–400°C; this low softening temperature is not suitable for most laboratory work. Besides, soft glass has a high thermal coefficient of expansion. This means that soft glass expands or contracts very rapidly when heated or cooled; sudden, rapid changes in temperature introduce too much stress into the material, and the glass cracks.

The beakers, Erlenmeyer flasks, and test tubes used in our laboratory experiments are composed of borosilicate glass and will withstand the heating and cooling required.

LABORATORY MEASUREMENTS

Units of Measurement

The metric system of weights and measures is used by scientists of all fields, including chemists. This system uses the base 10 for measurements; for conversions, measurements may be multiplied or divided by

Table 1.1 *Frequently Used Factors*

Prefix	Power of 10	Decimal Equivalent	Abbreviation
Micro	10^{-6}	0.000001	μ
Milli	10^{-3}	0.001	m
Centi	10^{-2}	0.01	c
Kilo	10^{3}	1000	k

Table 1.2 *Units and Equipment*

Measure	SI Unit	Metric Unit	Equipment
Length	Meter (m)	Meter (m)	Meterstick
Volume	Cubic meter (m^3)	Liter (L)	Pipet, graduated cylinder, Erlenmeyer flask, beaker
Mass	Kilogram (kg)	Gram (g)	Balance
Energy	Joule (J)	Calorie (cal)	Calorimeter
Temperature	Kelvin (K)	Degree Celsius (°C)	Thermometer

some factor of 10. Table 1.1 lists the most frequently used factors in the laboratory, which are based on powers of 10.

The measures of length, volume, mass, energy, and temperature are used to evaluate our physical and chemical environment. Table 1.2 compares the metric system with the more recently accepted SI system (International System of Units). The laboratory equipment associated with obtaining these measures is also listed.

Accuracy, precision, and significant figures

Chemistry is a science that depends on experience and observation for data. It is an empirical science. An experiment that yields data requires the appropriate measuring devices in order to get accurate measurements. Once the data is in hand, calculations are done with the numbers obtained. How good the calculations are depends on a number of factors: (1) how careful you are in taking the measurements (laboratory techniques), (2) how good your measuring device is in getting a true measure (accuracy), and (3) how reproducible the measurement is (precision).

The measuring device usually contains a scale. The scale, with its subdivisions or graduations, tells the limits of the device's accuracy. You cannot expect to obtain a measurement better than your instrument is capable of reading. Consider the portion of the ruler shown in Figure 1.2.

There are major divisions labeled at intervals of 1 cm and subdivisions of 0.1 cm or 1 mm. The accuracy of the ruler is to 0.1 cm (or 1 mm); that is the measurement that is known for certain. However, it is possible to estimate to 0.01 cm (or 0.1 mm) by reading in between the subdivisions; this number is less accurate and, of course, is less certain. In general, you should be able to record the measured value to one more place than the

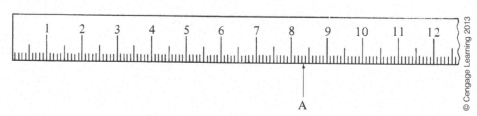

Figure 1.2
Reading a metric ruler.

scale is marked. For example, in Figure 1.2 there is a reading marked on the ruler. This value is 8.35 cm: two numbers are known with certainty, *8.3*, and one number, 0.05, is uncertain since it is the *best estimate* of the fractional part of the subdivision. The number recorded, 8.35, contains 3 significant figures, 2 certain plus 1 uncertain. When dealing with *significant figures,* remember: (1) the uncertainty is in the last recorded digit, and (2) the number of significant figures contains the number of digits definitely known, plus one more that is estimated.

The manipulation of significant figures in multiplication, division, addition, and subtraction is important. It is particularly important when using electronic calculators, which give many more digits than are useful or significant. If you keep in mind the principle that the final answer can be no more accurate than the least accurate measurement, you should not go wrong. A few examples will demonstrate this.

Example 1 Divide 9.3 by 4.05. If this calculation is done by a calculator, the answer found is 2.296296296. However, *a division should have as an answer the same number of significant figures as the least accurately known (fewest significant figures), of the numbers being divided.* One of the numbers, 9.3, contains only 2 significant figures. Therefore, the answer can only have 2 significant figures, i.e., 2.3 (rounded off).

Example 2 Multiply 0.31 by 2.563. Using a calculator, the answer is 0.79453. *As in division, a multiplication can have as an answer the same number of significant figures as the least accurately known (fewest significant figures), of the numbers being multiplied.* The number 0.31 has 2 significant figures (the zero fixes the decimal point). Therefore, the answer can only have 2 significant figures, i.e., 0.79 (rounded off).

Example 3 Add 3.56 + 4.321 + 5.9436. A calculator gives 13.8246. *With addition (or subtraction), the answer is significant to the least number of decimal places of the numbers added (or subtracted).* The least accurate number is 3.56, measured only to the hundredth's place. The answer should be to this accuracy, i.e., 13.82 (rounded off to the hundredth's place).

Example 4 Do the subtraction 6.532 − 1.3. A calculator gives 5.232 as the answer. However, since the least accurate number is 1.3, measured to the tenth's place, the answer should be to this accuracy, i.e., 5.2 (rounded off to the tenth's place).

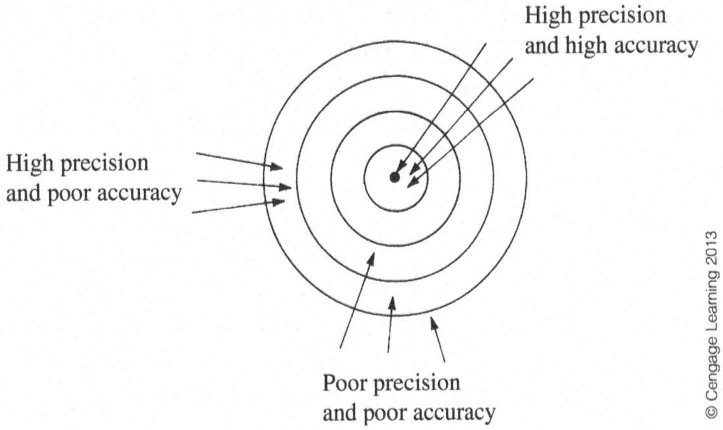

Figure 1.3
Precision and accuracy illustrated by a target.

Finally, how do precision and accuracy compare? *Precision* is a determination of the reproducibility of a measurement. It tells you how closely several measurements agree with one another. Several measurements of the same quantity showing high precision will cluster together with little or no variation in value; however, if the measurements show a wide variation, the precision is low. *Random errors* are errors that lead to differences in successive values of a measurement and affect precision; some values will be off in one direction or another. One can estimate the precision for a set of values for a given quantity as follows: estimate $= \pm \Delta/2$, where Δ is the difference between the highest and lowest values.

Accuracy is a measure of how closely the value determined agrees with a known or accepted value. Accuracy is subject to *systematic errors*. These errors cause measurements to vary from the known value and will be off in the same direction, either too high or too low. A consistent error in a measuring device will affect the accuracy, but always in the same direction. It is important to use properly calibrated measuring devices. If a measuring device is not properly calibrated, it may give high precision, but none of the measurements will be accurate. However, a properly calibrated measuring device will be both precise and accurate. (See Figure 1.3.) A systematic error is expressed as the difference between the known value and the average of the values obtained by measurement in a number of trials.

OBJECTIVES

1. To learn how to use a Bunsen burner.

2. To learn how to use simple, common equipment found in the laboratory.

3. To learn to take measurements.

4. To be able to record these measurements with precision and accuracy using the proper number of significant figures.

PROCEDURE

The Laboratory Gas Burner; Use of the Bunsen Burner

1. Before connecting the Bunsen burner to the gas source, examine the burner and compare it to Figure 1.1. Be sure to locate the gas control valve and the air vents and see how they work.

2. Connect the gas inlet of your burner to the main gas valve by means of a short piece of thin-walled rubber tubing. Be sure the tubing is long enough to provide some slack for movement on the bench top. Close the gas control valve. If your burner has a screw-needle valve, turn the knob clockwise. Close the air vents. This can be done by rotating the barrel of the burner.

3. Turn the main gas valve to the open position. Slowly open the gas control valve counterclockwise until you hear the hiss of gas. Quickly strike a match or use a gas striker to light the burner. With a lighted match, hold the flame to the top of the barrel. The gas should light. How would you describe the color of the flame (1)? Hold a Pyrex® test tube in this flame. What do you observe (2)?

4. Carefully turn the gas control valve, first clockwise and then counterclockwise. What happens to the flame size (3)? (If the flame should go out, or if the flame did not light initially, shut off the main gas valve and start over, as described above.)

5. With the flame on, adjust the air vents by rotating the barrel. What happens to the flame as the air vents open (4)? Adjust the gas control valve and the air vents until you obtain a flame about 3 or 4 in. high, with an inner cone of blue (Figure 1.1). The tip of the pale-blue inner cone is the hottest part of the flame.

6. Too much air will blow out the flame. Should this occur, close the main gas valve immediately. Relight following the procedure in step 3.

7. Too much gas pressure will cause the flame to rise away from the burner and "roar" (Figure 1.4). If this happens, reduce the gas flow by closing the gas control valve until a proper flame results.

8. "Flashback" sometimes occurs. If so, the burner will have a flame at the bottom of the barrel. Quickly close the main gas valve. Allow the barrel to cool. Relight following the procedures in step 3.

Figure 1.4
*The flame rises away
from the burner.*

Laboratory Measurements

Length: use of the meterstick (or metric ruler)

1. The meterstick is used to measure length. Examine the meterstick in your kit. You will notice that one side has its divisions in inches (in.) with subdivisions in sixteenths of an inch; the other side is in centimeters (cm) with subdivisions in millimeters (mm). Some useful conversion factors are listed below.

1 km = 1000 m	1 in. = 2.54 cm
1 m = 100 cm	1 ft. = 30.48 cm
1 cm = 10 mm	1 yd. = 91.44 cm
1 m = 1000 mm	1 mi. = 1.6 km

A meterstick that is calibrated to 0.1 cm can be read to the hundredth's place; however, only a 0 (0.00) or a 5 (0.05) may appear. A measurement falling directly on a subdivision is read as a 0 in the hundredth's place. A measurement falling anywhere between adjacent subdivisions is read as a 5 in the hundredth's place.

2. With your meterstick (or metric ruler), measure the length and width of this laboratory manual. Take the measurements in centimeters (to the nearest 0.01 cm). Record your response on the Report Sheet (1).

3. Convert the readings in cm to mm and m **(2)**.

4. Calculate the area of the manual in cm^2 and mm^2 **(3)**. Be sure to express your answers to the proper number of significant figures.

Example 5

A student measured a piece of paper and found it to be 20.30 cm by 29.25 cm. The area was found to be

$$20.30\,\text{cm} \times 29.25\,\text{cm} = 593.8\,\text{cm}^2$$

Volume: use of a graduated cylinder, an Erlenmeyer flask, and a beaker

1. Volume in the metric system is expressed in liters (L) and milliliters (mL). Another way of expressing milliliters is in cubic centimeters (cm^3 or cc). Several conversion factors for volume measurements are listed below.

1 L = 1000 mL	1 qt. = 0.96 L
1 mL = 1 cm^3 = 1 cc	1 gal. = 3.79 L
1 L = 0.26 gal.	1 fl. oz. = 29.6 mL

2. The graduated cylinder is a piece of glassware used for measuring the volume of a liquid. Graduated cylinders come in various sizes with different degrees of accuracy. A convenient size for this experiment is the 100-mL graduated cylinder. Note that this cylinder is marked in units of 1 mL; major divisions are of 10 mL and subdivisions are of 1 mL. Estimates can be made to the nearest 0.1 mL. When a liquid is in the graduated cylinder, you will see that the level in the cylinder is curved with the lowest point at the center. This is the *meniscus,* or the dividing line between liquid and air. When reading the meniscus for the volume, be sure to read the *lowest* point on the curve and not the upper edge. To avoid errors in reading the meniscus, the eye's line of sight must be perpendicular to the scale (Figure 1.5). In steps 3 and 4, use the graduated cylinder to see how well the marks on an Erlenmeyer flask and a beaker measure the indicated volume.

3. Take a 50-mL graduated Erlenmeyer flask (Figure 1.6) and fill with water to the 50-mL mark. Transfer the water, completely and without spilling, to a 100-mL graduated cylinder. Record the volume on the Report Sheet **(1)** to the nearest 0.1 mL; convert to L.

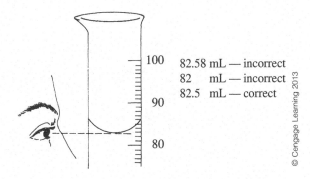

Figure 1.5
Reading the meniscus on a graduated cylinder.

82.58 mL — incorrect
82   mL — incorrect
82.5 mL — correct

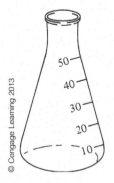

Figure 1.6
A 50-mL graduated Erlenmeyer flask.

Figure 1.7
A 50-mL graduated beaker.

4. Take a 50-mL graduated beaker (Figure 1.7), and fill with water to the 40-mL mark. Transfer the water, completely and without spilling, to a dry 100-mL graduated cylinder. Record the volume on the Report Sheet **(2)** to the nearest 0.1 mL; convert to L.

5. What is the error in mL and in percent for obtaining 50.0 mL for the Erlenmeyer flask and 40.0 mL for the beaker **(3)**? Calculate the % error using the equation on page 14.

6. Which piece of glassware will give you a more accurate measure of liquid: the graduated cylinder, the Erlenmeyer flask, or the beaker **(4)**?

Mass: use of the laboratory balance

1. Mass measurements of objects are carried out with the laboratory balance. Many types of balances are available for laboratory use. The proper choice of a balance depends upon what degree of accuracy is needed for a measurement. The standard units of mass are the kilogram (kg) in the SI system and the gram (g) in the metric system. Some conversion factors are listed below.

1 kg = 1000 g	1 lb. = 454 g	1 kg = 2.20 lb
1 g = 1000 mg	1 oz. = 28.35 g	

Two types of balances are illustrated in Figures 1.8 and 1.10. A platform triple beam balance is shown in Figure 1.8. This balance can weigh objects up to 2610 g. Because the scale is marked in 0.1-g divisions, it is mostly used for rough weighing; weights to 0.01 g can be estimated. Figure 1.9 illustrates how to take a reading on this balance.

A top-loading balance shows the highest accuracy (Figure 1.10). Mass measurements can be determined very rapidly with this balance because the total mass, to the nearest 0.001 g, can be read directly from a digital readout (Figure 1.10). A balance of this type is very expensive and should be used only after the instructor has demonstrated its use.

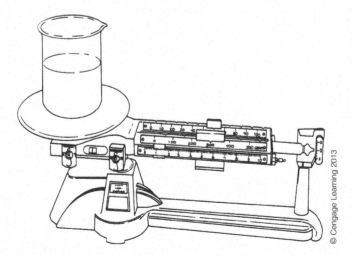

Figure 1.8
A platform triple beam balance.

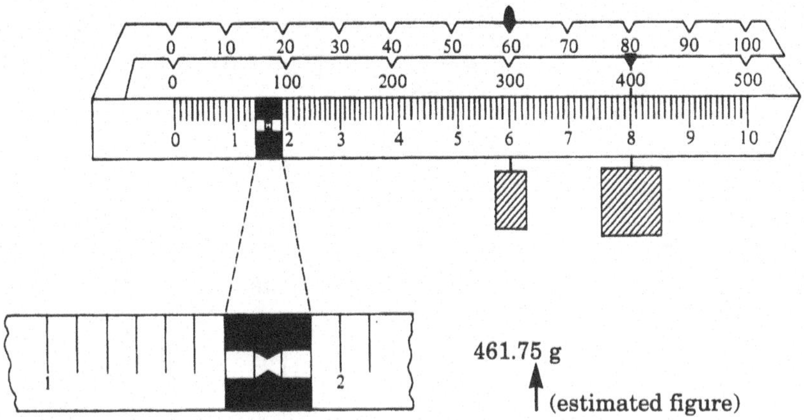

Figure 1.9
Reading on a platform triple beam balance.

461.75 g
↑ (estimated figure)

© Cengage Learning 2013

Figure 1.10
A top-loading balance with a digital readout.

© Cengage Learning 2013

CAUTION

When using any balance, never drop an object onto the pan; place it gently in the center of the pan. Never place chemicals directly on the pan; use either a glass container (watch glass, beaker, weighing bottle) or weighing paper. Never get the mass of a hot object; hot objects may mar the pan. Buoyancy effects will cause incorrect mass determinations. Clean up any chemical spills in the balance area to prevent damage to the balance.

---

2. Determine the mass of a quarter, a test tube (100 × 13 mm), and a 125-mL Erlenmeyer flask. Express each mass to the proper number of significant figures. Use a platform triple beam balance and a top-loading balance for these measurements. Use the table on the Report Sheet to record each mass.

Temperature: use of the thermometer

1. Routine measurements of temperature are done with a thermometer. Thermometers found in chemistry laboratories may use either mercury or a colored fluid as the liquid, and degrees Celsius (°C) as the units of measurement. The fixed reference points on this scale are the freezing point of water, 0°C, and the boiling point of water, 100°C. Between these two reference points, the scale is divided into 100 units, with each unit equal to 1°C. Temperature can be estimated to 0.1°C. Other thermometers use either the Fahrenheit (°F), or the Kelvin (K), temperature scale and use

the same reference points, that is, the freezing and boiling points of water. Conversion between the scales can be accomplished using the formulas below.

$$°F = \frac{9}{5}(°C) + 32.0 \qquad °C = \frac{5}{9}(°F - 32.0) \qquad K = °C + 273.15$$

Example 6

Convert 37.0°C to °F and K.

$$°F = \frac{9}{5}(37.0°C) + 32.0 = 98.6°F$$

$$K = 37.0°C + 273.15 = 310.2\,K$$

---

2. Use the thermometer in your kit and record, to the nearest 0.1°C, the temperature of the laboratory at *room temperature.* Use the Report Sheet to record your results.

3. Record the temperature of boiling water. Set up a 250-mL beaker containing 100 mL water, and heat on a hot plate until boiling. Hold the thermometer in the boiling water for at least 1 min. before reading the temperature (*be sure not to touch the sides of the beaker*). Using the Report Sheet, record your results to the nearest 0.1°C.

4. Record the temperature of ice water. Into a 250-mL beaker, add enough crushed ice to fill halfway. Add distilled water to the level of the ice. Stir the ice water gently with a glass rod for 1 min. before reading the thermometer. Hold the thermometer in the ice water for at least 1 min. before reading the temperature. *Use caution; be careful not to touch the walls of the beaker with the thermometer or to hit the thermometer with the glass rod.* Read the thermometer to the nearest 0.1°C. Record your results on the Report Sheet.

CAUTION

When reading the thermometer, do not hold the thermometer by the bulb. Body temperature will give an incorrect reading. If you are using a mercury thermometer and the thermometer breaks accidentally, call the instructor for proper disposal of the mercury. Mercury is toxic and very hazardous to your health. Do not handle the liquid or breathe its vapor.

---

5. Convert your answers to steps 2, 3, and 4 into °F and K.

CHEMICALS AND EQUIPMENT

1. Bunsen burner

2. 50-mL graduated beaker

3. 50-mL graduated Erlenmeyer flask

4. 100-mL graduated cylinder

5. Test tube (100 × 13 mm)

6. Meterstick or ruler

7. Quarter

8. Balances

9. Hot plates

1   E X P E R I M E N T 1

Pre-Lab Questions

1. Why is heat often used in a laboratory experiment?

2. What advantages does Pyrex glass have over regular soft glass as the material used to make laboratory glassware?

3. What does it mean for a series of measurements to be (a) accurate, and (b) precise?

4. Perform the following calculations and report your answer to the proper number of significant figures:

   a. $21.65 - 3.2 =$

   b. $4.01 / (4.583 + 2.108) =$

   c. $6.15 / 1.2 =$

   d. $2.26 \times 21.43 =$

name _____   section _____ date _____

partner _____   grade _____

Report Sheet

Bunsen burner

1. What color is the flame when the air vents are closed?

2. Did anything happen to the surface of the Pyrex® test tube in this flame?

3. What happens to the flame size when the gas control valve is turned?

4. Describe the effect on the flame as the air vents were opened.

Length

1. Length _____ cm

   Width _____ cm

2. Length _____ mm   _____ m

   Width _____ mm   _____ m

3. Area _____ cm² _____ mm²
   (Show calculations)

Volume

1. Erlenmeyer flask _____ mL   _____ L

2. Beaker   _____ mL   _____ L

3. Error in volume:

Erlenmeyer flask _____ mL   _____ %

Beaker   _____ mL   _____ %

$$\% \text{ Error} = \frac{\text{Error in volume}}{\text{Total volume}} \times 100 \quad \text{(Show your calculations.)}$$

4. _____

Mass

Object	Balance			
	Platform, triple Beam		Top Loading	
	g	mg	g	mg
Quarter				
Test tube (100 × 13 mm)				
125-mL Erlenmeyer flask				

Temperature

	°C	°F	K
Room temperature			
Ice water			
Boiling water			

How well do your thermometer readings agree with the accepted values for the freezing point and boiling point of water? Express any discrepancy as a deviation in degrees.

Post-Lab Questions

1. What would need to be done to a Bunsen burner in order to change a luminous yellow flame into a nonluminous blue flame?

2. If you needed exactly 45.3 mL of a solution, what piece of glass ware should you use? Justify your choice.

3. A student measured the dimensions of a table and recorded the length as 103.50 cm and the width as 73.75 cm. According to the student's calculator, the area is 7633.125 cm^2. What value should the student report as the area? Explain your answer.

4. John has a mass of 115 kg. Sally has a mass of 115 lb. Who is the heaver of the two and by how much? Show your calculations to justify your answer.

5. At 20,320 ft., Alaska's Mount McKinley is the highest peak in North America. Express this height in meters (m), and kilometers (km), to the correct number of significant figures. Show your work.

6. A 16.95 g sample of sugar was added to a glass with a mass of 8.30 oz. What is the combined mass of the glass and the sample in ounces (oz.), grams (g), and milligrams (mg)? Show your work and express your answers to the correct number of significant figures.

Density Determination

BACKGROUND

Samples of matter can be identified by using characteristic physical properties. A substance may have a unique color, odor, melting point, or boiling point. These properties do not depend on the quantity of the substance and are called *intensive properties*. Density is also an intensive property and may serve as a means of identification.

The *density* of a substance is the *ratio of its mass per unit volume*. Density can be found mathematically by dividing the mass of a substance by its volume. The formula is $d = \frac{m}{V}$, where d is density, m is mass, and V is volume. Whereas mass and volume do depend on the quantity of a substance (these are *extensive properties*), the ratio is constant at a given temperature. The unit of density, reported in standard references, is in terms of g/mL (or g/cc or g/cm^3) at 20°C. The temperature is reported because the volume of a sample will change with temperature and, thus, so does the density.

Example

A bank received a yellow bar, marked gold, with a mass of 453.6 g, and a volume of 23.5 cm^3. Is it gold? (Density of gold = 19.3 g/cm^3 at 20°C.)

$$d = \frac{m}{V} = \frac{453.6 \text{ g}}{23.5 \text{ cm}^3} = 19.3 \text{ g/cm}^3$$

Yes, it is gold.

OBJECTIVES

1. To determine the densities of regular- and irregular-shaped objects and use them as a means of identification.

2. To determine the density of water.

3. To determine the density of a liquid and use this as a means of identification.

PROCEDURE

Density of a
Regular-Shaped Object

1. Obtain a solid block from your instructor. Record the code number.

2. Using your metric ruler, determine the dimensions of the block (length, width, height), and record the values to the nearest 0.05 cm **(1)**. Calculate the volume of the block **(2)**. Repeat the measurements for a second trial.

3. Using a top-loading balance, determine the mass of the block **(3)**. Record the mass to the nearest 0.001 g. Calculate the density of the block **(4)**. Repeat the measurements for a second trial.

Density of an
Irregular-Shaped Object

1. Obtain a sample of unknown metal from your instructor. Record the code number.

2. Obtain a mass of the sample of approximately 5 g. Be sure to record the exact quantity to the nearest 0.001 g **(5)**.

3. Choose either a 10-mL (for small metal pieces), or a 25-mL graduated cylinder (for larger metal pieces). Fill the graduated cylinder approximately halfway with water. Record the exact volume to the nearest 0.05 mL **(6)**. [Depending on the number of subdivisions between milliliter divisions, you may be able to read to the hundredth's place. For example, you can read the 10-mL graduated cylinder to the hundredth's place where only a 0 (the reading is directly on a subdivision, e.g., 0.00), or a 5 (anywhere between two adjacent subdivisions, e.g., 0.05), can be used.]

4. Place the metal sample into the graduated cylinder. (If the pieces of metal are too large for the opening of the 10-mL graduated cylinder, use the larger graduated cylinder.) Be sure all of the metal is below the water line. Gently tap the sides of the cylinder with your fingers to ensure that no air bubbles are trapped in the metal. Read the new level of the water in the graduated cylinder to the nearest 0.05 mL **(7)**. Assuming that the metal does not dissolve or react with the water, the difference between the two levels represents the volume of the metal sample **(8)** (Figure 2.1).

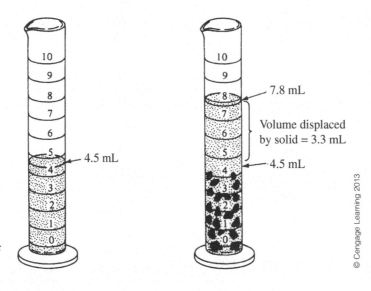

Figure 2.1
Measurement of the volume of
an irregular-shaped object.

Table 2.1 *Densities of Selected Metals*

Sample	Formula	Density (g/cm³)
Aluminum	Al	2.70
Iron	Fe	7.86
Tin (white)	Sn	7.29
Zinc	Zn	7.13
Lead	Pb	11.30

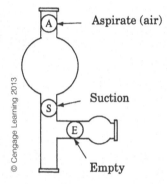

Aspirate (air)

Suction

Empty

© Cengage Learning 2013

Figure 2.2
The Spectroline® pipet filler.

5. Carefully recover the metal sample and dry it with a paper towel. Repeat the experiment with another sample of your unknown for a second trial.

6. Calculate the density of the metal sample from your data **(9)**. Determine the average density from your trials, reporting to the proper number of significant figures.

7. Determine the identity of your metal sample by comparing its density to the densities listed in Table 2.1 **(10)**.

8. Recover your metal sample and return it as directed by your instructor.

CAUTION

Do not discard the samples in waste containers or in the sink. Use the labeled collection container that is specific for each sample.

Use of the Spectroline® Pipet Filler

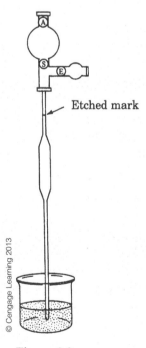

Etched mark

© Cengage Learning 2013

Figure 2.3
Using the Spectroline® pipet filler to pipet.

COPYRIGHT © 2013 Cengage Learning

1. Examine the Spectroline® pipet filler and locate the valves marked "A," "S," and "E" (Figure 2.2). These operate by pressing the flat surfaces between the thumb and forefinger.

2. Squeeze the bulb with one hand while you press valve "A" with two fingers of the other hand. The bulb flattens as air is expelled. If you release your fingers when the bulb is flattened, the bulb remains collapsed.

3. Carefully insert the pipet end into the Spectroline® pipet filler (Figure 2.3). The end should insert easily and not be forced.

CAUTION

Before inserting the pipet end into the Spectroline® pipet filler, lubricate the glass by rubbing the opening with a drop of water or glycerin.

4. Place the tip of the pipet into the liquid to be pipetted. Make sure that the tip is below the surface of the liquid at all times.

5. With your thumb and forefinger, press valve "S." Liquid will be drawn up into the pipet. By varying the pressure applied by your fingers, the rise of the liquid into the pipet can be controlled. Allow the liquid to fill the pipet to a level slightly above the etched mark on the stem. Release the valve; the liquid should remain in the pipet.

6. Withdraw the pipet from the liquid. Draw the tip of the pipet lightly along the wall of the beaker to remove excess liquid.

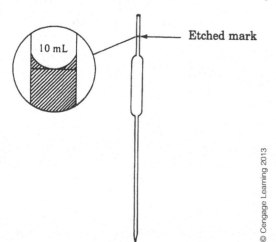

← Etched mark

© Cengage Learning 2013

Figure 2.4
Adjusting the curved meniscus of the liquid to the etched mark.

7. Adjust the level of the meniscus of the liquid by carefully pressing valve "E." The level should lower until the curved meniscus touches the etched mark (Figure 2.4). Carefully draw the tip of the pipet lightly along the wall of the beaker to remove excess liquid.

8. Drain the liquid from the pipet into a collection flask by pressing valve "E." Remove any drops on the tip by touching the tip of the pipet against the inside walls of the collection flask. Liquid should remain inside the tip; the pipet is calibrated with this liquid in the tip. Do not blow out the liquid that is caught in the pipette tip.

CAUTION

Never use your mouth when pipetting. Always use a pipet filler.

Density of an Unknown Liquid

1. Obtain approximately 25 mL of an unknown liquid from your instructor. Record the code number. Determine the temperature of the liquid **(11)**.

2. Determine the mass of a clean, dry 50-mL beaker to the nearest 0.001 g **(12)**.

3. Transfer 10.00 mL of the liquid with a 10-mL volumetric pipet into the preweighed beaker using the Spectroline® pipet filler (Figure 2.2). Immediately determine the mass of the beaker to the nearest 0.001 g **(13)**.

4. Calculate the mass of the unknown liquid by subtraction **(14)**.

5. Calculate the density of the unknown liquid at the temperature recorded **(15)**.

6. Repeat the procedure, following steps 1–5, for a second trial. When you repeat the steps, be sure all the glassware is clean and dry.

7. Calculate the average density. Determine the identity of your unknown liquid by comparing its density to the densities listed in Table 2.2 **(16)**.

8. Discard your used liquid samples into containers provided by your instructor. Do not pour them into the sink.

Table 2.2 *Densities of Selected Liquids*

Sample	Density (g/mL)	T (°C)
Hexane	0.659	20
Ethanol	0.791	20
Olive oil	0.918	15
Seawater	1.025	20 (3.15 g NaCl/100 g solution)
Milk	1.028–1.035	20
Ethylene glycol	1.109	20

CHEMICALS AND EQUIPMENT

1. Spectroline® pipet filler
2. 10-mL volumetric pipet
3. Solid woodblock
4. Aluminum
5. Iron
6. Lead
7. Tin
8. Zinc
9. Hexane
10. Ethanol
11. Ethylene glycol
12. Milk
13. Olive oil
14. Seawater

2   EXPERIMENT 2

Pre-Lab Questions

1. How does an *intensive* property differ from an *extensive* property? Give an example of an intensive property and of an extensive property.

2. To calculate the density of a solid or liquid sample, what two measurements are needed?

3. A solid block having a volume of exactly 100.0 cm^3 has a mass of 153.6 g. Calculate the block's density. Will the block sink or float in water?

4. A salvage operator recovered coins believed to be gold. A sample had a mass of 129.6 g and had a volume of 15.3 cm^3. Were the coins gold (d = 19.3 g/cm^3) or just yellow brass (d = 8.47 g/cm^3)? Show your work.

name _____   section _____   date _____

partner _____   grade _____

2   **E X P E R I M E N T 2**

Report Sheet

Report all measurements and calculations to the correct number of significant figures.

Density of a regular-shaped object	*Trial 1*	*Trial 2*

Unknown code number _____

1. Length	_____ cm	_____ cm
Width	_____ cm	_____ cm
Height	_____ cm	_____ cm
2. Volume (L × W × H)	_____ cm^3	_____ cm^3
3. Mass	_____ g	_____ g
4. Density: (3)/(2)	_____ g/cm^3	_____ g/cm^3
Average density of block	_____ g/cm^3	

Density of an irregular-shaped object	*Trial 1*	*Trial 2*

Unknown code number _____

5. Mass of metal sample	_____ g	_____ g
6. Initial volume of water	_____ mL	_____ mL
7. Final volume of water	_____ mL	_____ mL
8. Volume of metal: (7) − (6)	_____ mL	_____ mL
9. Density of metal: (5)/(8)	_____ g/mL	_____ g/mL
Average density of metal	_____ g/mL	

10. Identity of unknown metal _____

Density of an unknown liquid   *Trial 1*   *Trial 2*

Unknown code number_____

11. Temperature of unknown liquid   _____ °C   _____ °C

12. Mass of 50-mL beaker   _____ g   _____ g

   Volume of liquid   10.00 mL   10.00 mL

13. Mass of beaker and liquid   _____ g   _____ g

14. Mass of liquid: (13) − (12)   _____ g   _____ g

15. Density of liquid: (14)/10.00 mL   _____ g/mL   _____ g/mL

   Average density of unknown liquid   _____ g/mL

16. Identity of unknown liquid _____

Post-Lab Questions

1. Two students set out to identify an unknown liquid based on its density. One student took exactly 25.00 mL and found the mass to be 22.95 g. A second student took exactly 50.00 mL and found the mass to be 45.90 g.

    a. Calculate the density of each sample and identify the liquid(s). (see Table 2.2)

    b. Are the densities the same? If yes, is this what you expected? If no, why not?

2. A liquid sample, with a density of 0.915 g/mL, has a mass of 17.7 grams.

    a. What is the volume of this sample (in mL)?

    b. What mass (in grams), of this sample would have a volume of 76.5 mL?

3. In the density determination of a liquid, it was necessary to use the volumetric pipet properly. A student needed to deliver exactly 50.0 mL of a liquid. How will the quantity of liquid delivered, and the density determined, be affected by the situations described below? i.e., will the quantities be higher, lower, or unchanged? Explain your choice.

    a. The student did not allow sufficient time for all the liquid to empty from the pipet.

    b. The student allowed all the liquid to drain and then blew out the small amount from the tip.

    c. Air bubbles were not removed from the pipet before delivering the liquid.

Separation of the Components of a Mixture

BACKGROUND

Mixtures are not unique to chemistry; we use and consume them on a daily basis. The beverages we drink each morning, the fuel we use in our automobiles, and the ground we walk on are mixtures. Very few materials we encounter are pure. Any material made up of two or more substances that are not chemically combined is a mixture.

Isolating the pure components of a mixture requires the separation of one component from another. Chemists have developed techniques for doing this. These methods take advantage of the differences in physical properties of the components. The techniques to be demonstrated in this laboratory are the following:

1. *Sublimation*. This involves heating a solid until it passes directly from the solid phase into the gaseous phase. The reverse process, when the vapor goes back to the solid phase without a liquid state in between, is called deposition. Examples of solids that sublime are iodine, caffeine, and naphthalene (mothballs).

2. *Extraction*. This uses a solvent to selectively dissolve one or more components from a solid mixture. With this technique, a soluble solid can be separated from an insoluble solid.

3. *Decantation*. This separates a liquid from an insoluble solid sediment by carefully pouring the liquid from the solid without disturbing the solid (Figure 3.1).

4. *Filtration*. This separates a solid from a liquid through the use of a porous material as a filter. Paper, charcoal, or sand can serve as a filter. These materials allow the liquid to pass through but not the solid (see Figure 3.4 in the **Procedure** section).

5. *Evaporation*. This is the process of heating a mixture in order to drive off, in the form of vapor, a volatile liquid, so as to make the remaining component dry.

All of these techniques involve changes in the physical state of a chemical compound, whether it is as a solid, liquid, gas, or present in a solution; no chemical bonds have been broken in undergoing a

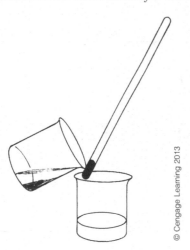

Figure 3.1
Decantation.

© Cengage Learning 2013

transformation from one state to another. In contrast, a change in the chemical state would require the making and/or breaking of chemical bonds.

The mixture that will be separated in this experiment contains three components: naphthalene ($C_{10}H_8$), common table salt (NaCl), and sea sand (SiO_2). The separation will be done according to the scheme in Figure 3.2 by:

1. heating the mixture to sublime the naphthalene,

2. dissolving the table salt with water to extract, and

3. evaporating water to recover dry NaCl and sand.

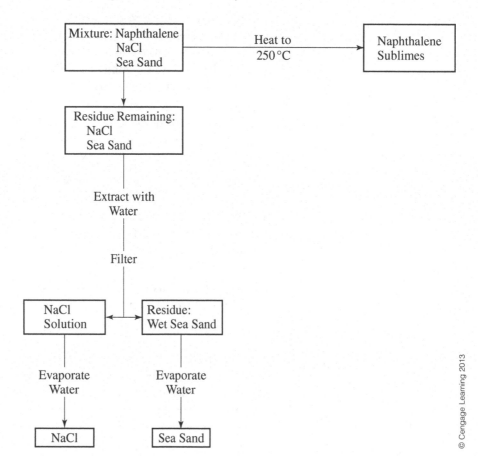

Figure 3.2
Separation scheme.

© Cengage Learning 2013

1. To demonstrate the separation of a mixture.

2. To examine some techniques for separation using physical methods.

PROCEDURE

1. Obtain a clean, dry 150-mL beaker and carefully determine the mass to the nearest 0.001 g. Record the mass for beaker 1 on the Report Sheet **(1)**. Obtain a sample of the unknown mixture from your instructor; use a mortar and pestle to grind the mixture into a fine powder. With the beaker still on the balance, carefully transfer approximately 2 g of the unknown mixture into the beaker. Record the mass of the beaker with the contents to the nearest 0.001 g **(2)**. Calculate the exact mass of the sample by subtraction **(3)**.

2. Perform the sublimation in a fume hood, if possible. Place an evaporating dish on top of the beaker containing the mixture. Place the beaker and evaporating dish on a wire gauze with an iron ring and ring stand assembly as shown in Figure 3.3. A hot plate could be used instead of the Bunsen burner, if desired. Place ice in the evaporating dish, being careful not to get any water on the underside of the evaporating dish or inside the beaker.

3. Carefully heat the beaker with a Bunsen burner, increasing the intensity of the flame until vapors appear in the beaker. *Be careful no vapors escape.* (Again, a hot plate could be used instead of the Bunsen burner). A solid should collect on the underside of the evaporating dish. After 10 min. of heating, remove the Bunsen burner (or hot plate), from under the beaker. Carefully remove the evaporating dish from the beaker and collect the solid by scraping it off the dish with a spatula onto a weighing paper. Drain away any water from the evaporating dish and add ice to it, if necessary. Stir the contents of the beaker with a glass rod. Return the evaporating dish to the beaker and apply the heat again. Continue heating and scraping off solid until no

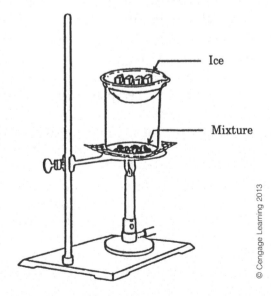

© Cengage Learning 2013

Figure 3.3
Assembly for sublimation.

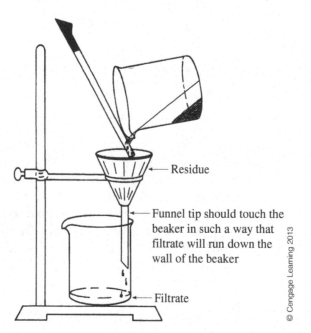

— Residue

— Funnel tip should touch the beaker in such a way that filtrate will run down the wall of the beaker

© Cengage Learning 2013

— Filtrate

Figure 3.4
Gravity filtration.

more solid collects. Weigh all the naphthalene collected and record the weight on the Report Sheet to the nearest 0.001 g **(4)**. Discard the naphthalene into the container provided.

4. Allow the beaker to cool until it reaches room temperature. Weigh the beaker with the contained solid **(5a)**. Calculate the mass of the naphthalene that sublimed **(5b)**.

5. Add about 25 mL of distilled water to the solid in beaker 1. Heat gently and stir continuously for 5 min. Do not let the mixture boil because it will "bump" and spatter the solid.

6. Weigh a second clean, dry 150-mL beaker with 2 or 3 boiling stones, to the nearest 0.001 g **(6)**.

7. Assemble the apparatus for gravity filtration as shown in Figure 3.4.

8. Weigh a piece of filter paper **(9)**. Fold the filter paper following the technique shown in Figure 3.5.

9. Wet the filter paper with water and adjust the paper so that it lies flat on the glass of the funnel.

10. Position beaker 2 under the funnel.

11. Pour the mixture through the filter, first decanting most of the liquid into beaker 2, and then carefully transferring the wet solid into the funnel with a rubber policeman. Collect all the liquid (called the filtrate) in beaker 2.

12. Rinse beaker 1 with 5–10 mL of water, pour over the residue in the funnel, and add the liquid to the filtrate; repeat with an additional 5–10 mL of water.

13. Place beaker 2 and its contents on a wire gauze with an iron ring and ring stand assembly as shown in Figure 3.6. Begin to heat gently with a Bunsen burner. Control the flame in order to prevent boiling over. This can also be done with a hot plate, if desired. As the volume of liquid is reduced, solid sodium chloride will appear. Reduce the flame (or turn down the hot plate), to avoid bumping of the solution and

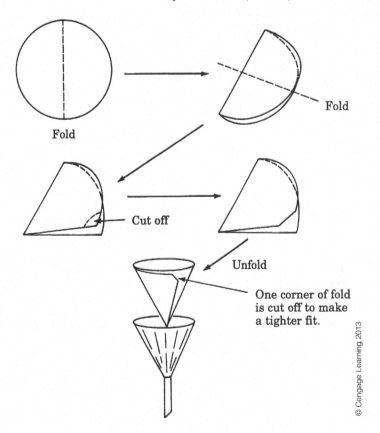

Figure 3.5
Steps for folding a filter paper for gravity filtration.

© Cengage Learning, 2013

spattering of the solid. When all of the liquid is gone, cool the beaker to room temperature. Determine the mass of the beaker, stones, and the solid residue to the nearest 0.001 g **(7)**. Calculate the mass of the recovered NaCl by subtraction **(8)**.

14. Carefully remove the filter paper and sand from the filter, open it up, and place it on a watch glass. Heat the sand to dryness in an oven at T = 90–100°C. Heat carefully to avoid spattering; when dry, the sand should be freely flowing. Allow the sand to cool to room temperature. Determine the mass of the filter paper and the sand to the nearest 0.001 g **(10)**. Calculate the mass of the recovered sand by subtraction **(11)**.

15. Calculate the:

    a. Percent yield **(13)** using the formula:

$$\% \text{ yield} = \frac{\textbf{grams of solid recovered (12)}}{\textbf{grams of initial sample (3)}} \times \textbf{100}$$

    b. Percentage of each component in the mixture by using the formula:

$$\% \text{ component} = \frac{\textbf{grams of component isolated}}{\textbf{grams of initial sample (3)}} \times \textbf{100}$$

Example

A student isolated the following from a sample weighing 1.132 g:

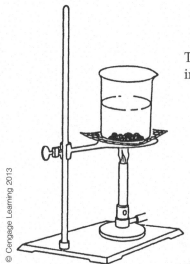

© Cengage Learning 2013

Evaporation of a volatile
liquid from a solution.

Figure 3.6
Assembly for evaporation.

0.170 g of naphthalene
0.443 g of NaCl
0.499 g of sand
———————————
1.112 g solid recovered

The student calculated the percent yield and percentage of each component in the mixture as follows:

$$\% \text{ yield} = \frac{1.112 \text{ g (solid recovered)}}{1.132 \text{ g (original sample)}} \times 100 = 98.2\%$$

$$\% \text{ C}_{10}\text{H}_8 = \frac{0.170 \text{ g (naphthalene)}}{1.132 \text{ g (original sample)}} \times 100 = 15.0\%$$

$$\% \text{ NaCl} = \frac{0.443 \text{ g (NaCl)}}{1.132 \text{ g (original sample)}} \times 100 = 39.1\%$$

$$\% \text{ sand} = \frac{0.499 \text{ g (sand)}}{1.132 \text{ g (original sample)}} \times 100 = 44.1\%$$

CHEMICALS AND EQUIPMENT

1. Unknown mixture
2. Balances
3. Boiling stones
4. Evaporating dish, 6 cm
5. Watch glass
6. Filter paper, 15 cm
7. Mortar and pestle
8. Oven (if available)
9. Ring stands (3)
10. Rubber policeman
11. Heat Source (Bunsen Burner or Hot Plate)

3 | **EXPERIMENT 3**

Pre-Lab Questions

1. I make my cup of coffee in the morning by pouring boiling water over ground-up coffee beans held in a special piece of paper and by collecting the brown liquid that comes through. Which techniques of the five described in the **Background** section is/are used in the preparation of the cup of coffee?

2. To sweeten the coffee from question 1 I add a tablespoon of sugar to my cup of coffee and the solid disappears. What makes up the "cup of coffee" now? Is this a mixture?

3. What is taking place during the process of sublimation? How is this process different from evaporation?

4. Do any of the techniques described in the **Background** section involve a chemical change? Explain your answer.

name _____   _section_ _____   _date_ _____

partner _____   _grade_ _____

| 3 | **EXPERIMENT 3** |

Report Sheet

1. Mass of beaker 1 _____ g

2. Mass of beaker 1 and mixture _____ g

3. Mass of mixture: (2) − (1) _____ g

4. Mass of naphthalene collected _____ g

5. a. Mass of beaker 1 and solid after sublimation _____ g

   b. Mass of naphthalene by difference: (2) − (5a) _____ g

6. Mass of beaker 2 _____ g

7. Mass of beaker 2 and NaCl _____ g

8. Mass of NaCl: (7) − (6) _____ g

9. Mass of filter paper _____ g

10. Mass of filter paper and sand _____ g

11. Mass of sand: (10) − (9) _____ g

Calculations

12. Mass of recovered solids:

   (5b) + (8) + (11) _____ g

13. Percent yield (percentage of solids recovered):

   $\% = [(12)/(3)] \times 100$ _____ %

14. Percentage of naphthalene:

   $\% = [(5b)/(3)] \times 100$ _____ %

15. Percentage of NaCl:

   $\% = [(8)/(3)] \times 100$ _____ %

16. Percentage of sand:

   $\% = [(11)/(3)] \times 100$ _____ %

Post-Lab Questions

1. A student completed the experiment but found that the total amount of material recovered weighed more than the original sample. What is the most likely cause of this error and how may it be corrected?

2. A student found that the mass of the naphthalene collected **(4)**, was less than the mass determined by difference **(5b)**. What would account for the smaller amount of naphthalene collected?

3. Mothballs in a clothes closet gradually disappear over time. What happens to this material?

4. In 100 g of sweet peas, there are 14.5 g carbohydrates, 5.7 g sugars, 5.1 g dietary fiber, 5.4 g protein, and 0.4 g fat.

   a. Calculate the percent composition for each of these components

   b. What percent, of the total mass of the sweet peas, do these substances account for?

   c. What substance makes up the majority of the remaining mass of the sweet peas?

Using Distillation to Separate the Components of a Mixture

BACKGROUND

Distillation is one of the most common methods of purifying a liquid. It is a very simple method: a liquid is brought to a boil, the liquid becomes a gas, the gas condenses and returns to the liquid state, and the liquid is collected.

Everyone has had an opportunity to heat water to a boil. As heat is applied, water molecules increase their kinetic energy. Some molecules acquire sufficient energy to escape from the liquid phase and enter into the vapor phase. Evaporation occurs this way. The vapor above the liquid exerts a pressure, called the vapor pressure. As more and more molecules obtain enough energy to escape into the vapor phase, the vapor pressure of these molecules increases. Eventually the vapor pressure equals the pressure exerted externally on the liquid (usually caused by the atmosphere). Boiling occurs at this point, and the temperature where this occurs is called the boiling point.

In distillation, the process described is carried out in an enclosed system, such as that illustrated in Figure 4.2. The liquid in the distilling flask is heated to a boil, and the vapor rises through tubing. The vapor then travels into a tube cooled by water, which serves as a condenser, where the vapor returns to the liquid state. If the mixture has a low-boiling component (a volatile substance with a high vapor pressure), it will distill first and can be collected. Higher-boiling and nonvolatile components (substances with low vapor pressure), remain in the boiling flask. Only by applying more heat will the higher-boiling component be distilled. Nonvolatile substances will not distill.

Normal distillations, procedures carried out at atmospheric pressure, require "normal" boiling points. However, when boiling takes place in a closed system, it is possible to change the boiling point of the liquid by changing the pressure in the closed system. If the external pressure is reduced, usually by using a vacuum pump or a water aspirator, the boiling point of the liquid is reduced. Thus, heat-sensitive liquids, some of which decompose when boiled at atmospheric pressure, distill with minimum decomposition at reduced pressure and temperature. The relationship between temperature and vapor pressure for the organic compound aniline is shown by the curve in

---

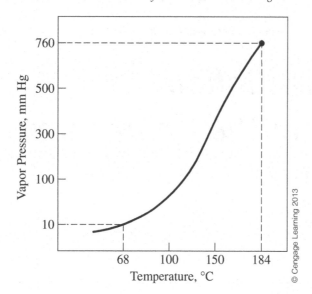

Figure 4.1

Temperature–vapor pressure curve for aniline.

Figure 4.1. Aniline, $C_6H_5NH_2$, a compound used to make synthetic dyes, can be distilled at 184°C (760 mm Hg), or at 68°C (10 mm Hg).

In this experiment a salt–water mixture will be separated by distillation. The volatile water will be separated from the nonvolatile salt (sodium chloride, NaCl). The purity of the collected distilled water will be demonstrated by chemical tests specific for sodium ions (Na^+) and chloride ions (Cl^-).

OBJECTIVES

1. To use distillation to separate a mixture.

2. To show that distillation can purify a liquid.

PROCEDURE

1. Assemble an apparatus like that in Figure 4.2. The distillation kit (obtained from your instructor), contains standard taper joints, which allow for quick assembly and disassembly. Before fitting the pieces together, apply a light coating of silicone grease to each joint to prevent the joints from sticking.

2. Use 100-mL round-bottom flasks for the distilling flask and the receiving flask. Fill the distilling flask with 50 mL of the prepared salt–water mixture. Add two boiling stones to the distilling flask to ensure smooth boiling of the mixture and to prevent bumping. Be sure that the rubber tubing to the condenser enters the lower opening and empties out of the upper opening. Turn on the water faucet and allow the water to fill the jacket of the condenser slowly, so as not to trap air. Take care not to provide too much flow, otherwise the hoses will disconnect from the condenser. Adjust the bulb of the thermometer so it is below the junction of the condenser and the distillation column. This is to ensure that the thermometer is immersed in the vapors resulting in a more accurate temperature determination. **Be sure that the opening of the vacuum adapter is always open to the atmosphere.**

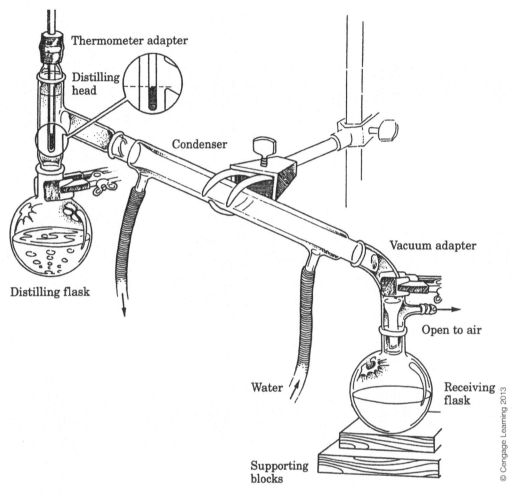

Thermometer adapter

Distilling head

Condenser

Vacuum adapter

Distilling flask

Open to air

Water

Receiving flask

Supporting blocks

© Cengage Learning 2013

Figure 4.2
A distillation apparatus.

3. Gently heat the distilling flask with a Bunsen burner or a heating mantle. Eventually the liquid will boil, vapors will rise and enter the condenser, and liquid will recondense and be collected in the receiving flask.

4. Discard the first 1 mL of water collected. Record the temperature of the vapors as soon as the 1 mL of water has been collected. Continue collection of the distilled water until approximately one-half of the mixture has distilled. Record the temperature of the vapors at this point **(3)**. Turn off the heat source and allow the system to return to room temperature.

5. The collected distilled water, the liquid left in the boiling flask, and a sample of pure distilled water from a tap will be tested.

6. Place in separate clean, dry test tubes (100 × 13 mm) 2 mL each of the three water samples described above in Step 5. Add, to each sample, 5 drops of silver nitrate solution. Look for the appearance of a white precipitate. Record your observations. Silver ions combine with chloride ions to form a white precipitate of silver chloride.

$$\text{Ag}^+ + \text{Cl}^- \longrightarrow \text{AgCl(s)} \text{ (White precipitate)}$$

7. Place in separate clean, dry test tubes (100 × 13 mm) 2 mL each of the three water samples described above in Step 5. Obtain a clean nickel wire from your instructor and hold the wire in a Bunsen burner flame until it burns red hot. Dip the wire into the distilled water sample. Put the wire into the Bunsen burner flame. Record the color of the flame. Repeat the above procedure (clean wire, dip into liquid, place into flame), for the other two samples. Record your observations. Sodium ions produce a bright yellow flame with a Bunsen burner.

8. Use paper towels to wipe the grease from the joints before cleaning the glassware used in the distillation.

CHEMICALS AND EQUIPMENT

1. Boiling stones
2. Bunsen burner
3. Clamps
4. Distillation kit
5. Silicone grease
6. Thermometer
7. Nickel wire
8. Salt–water mixture
9. 0.5 M silver nitrate, 0.5 M $AgNO_3$
10. Test tubes (100 × 13 mm)

EXPERIMENT 4

Pre-Lab Questions

1. a. What happens when the vapor pressure of water equals the external pressure exerted on its surface?

b. If this external pressure is caused by the atmosphere (i.e., 1.00 atm pressure), what do we call the temperature at this point?

2. If a mixture contained two compounds, volatile compound **A** and nonvolatile compound **B**, and this mixture was subjected to a distillation, which compound would distill and which one would be left behind?

3. You have a liquid that is heat-sensitive and decomposes when overheated. How can this material be purified by distillation without using excessive heat?

4. Why are you warned (in the **PROCEDURE** section), to ensure that the vacuum adaptor remains open?

4 **E X P E R I M E N T 4**

Report Sheet

1. Barometric pressure _____

2. Boiling point of water at measured pressure _____

3. Temperature of vapor after collecting 1 mL _____

4. Temperature of vapor at end of distillation _____

Solution	Observation with 0.5 M AgNO₃	Color in Flame Test
Distilled water collected		
Liquid in boiling flask		
Distilled water from tap		

Post-Lab Questions

1. What evidence is there in your experiment that the water collected in the receiving flask was salt free?

2. A mixture of cyclohexane (b.p. 81°C), and toluene (b.p. 111°C), are to be separated by distillation. As the temperature is increased, which liquid should distill first and why?

3. Using Figure 4.1, predict the approximate temperature at which aniline will boil when the pressure is reduced to (a) 400 mm Hg and (b) 100 mm Hg.

4. What would happen to the temperature reading if the thermometer bulb was placed above the junction of the condenser and the distilling column?

Physical Properties of Chemicals: Melting Point and Boiling Point

BACKGROUND

If you were asked to describe a friend, most likely you would start by identifying particular physical characteristics. You might begin by giving your friend's height, weight, hair color, eye color, or facial features. These characteristics would allow you to single out the individual from a group.

Chemicals also possess distinguishing physical properties which enable their identification. In many circumstances, a thorough determination of the physical properties of a given chemical can be used for its identification. If faced with an unknown sample, a chemist may compare the physical properties of the unknown to properties of known substances that are tabulated in the chemical literature; if a match can be made, an identification can be assumed (unless chemical evidence suggests otherwise).

The physical properties most commonly listed in handbooks of chemical data are color, crystal form (if a solid), refractive index (if a liquid), density, solubility in various solvents, melting point, sublimation characteristics, and boiling point. When a new compound is isolated or synthesized, these properties almost always accompany the report in the literature.

The transition of a substance from a solid to a liquid to a gas, and the reversal, represent physical changes. In a *physical change* there is only a change in the form or state of the substance. No chemical bonds break; no alteration in the chemical composition occurs. If chemical bonds are broken and reformed, and if there is a change in chemical composition, then there is a *chemical change*. Water undergoes state changes from ice to liquid water to steam; however, the composition of molecules in all three states remains H_2O.

$$H_2O(s) \rightleftharpoons H_2O(l) \rightleftharpoons H_2O(g)$$
$$\text{Ice} \qquad \text{Liquid} \qquad \text{Steam}$$

The *melting* or *freezing point* of a substance refers to the temperature at which the solid and liquid states are in equilibrium. The terms are interchangeable and correspond to the same temperature; how the terms are applied depends upon the state the substance is in originally. The melting point is the temperature at equilibrium when starting in the solid state and going to the liquid state. The freezing point is the temperature at equilibrium when starting in the liquid state and going to the solid state.

Melting points of pure substances occur over a very narrow range and are usually quite sharp. The criteria for purity of a solid are the narrowness of the melting point range and the correspondence to the value found in the literature. Impurities will lower the melting point and cause a broadening of the range. For example, pure benzoic acid has a reported melting point of 122.13°C; benzoic acid with a melting point range of 121–122°C is considered to be quite pure.

The *boiling point* or *condensation* point of a liquid refers to the temperature when its vapor pressure is equal to the external pressure. If a beaker of liquid is brought to a boil in your laboratory, bubbles of vapor form throughout the liquid. These bubbles rise rapidly to the surface, burst, and release vapor to the space above the liquid. In this case, the liquid is in contact with the atmosphere; the **normal** boiling point of the liquid will be the temperature when the pressure of the vapor is equal to the atmospheric pressure (1 atm or 760 mm Hg). Should the external pressure vary, so will the boiling point. A liquid will boil at a higher temperature when the external pressure is higher and will boil at a lower temperature when the external pressure is reduced. The change in state from a gas to a liquid represents condensation and is the reverse of boiling. The temperature for this change of state is the same as the boiling temperature but is concerned with the approach from the gas phase.

Just as a solid has a characteristic melting point, a liquid has a characteristic boiling point. At one atmosphere, pure water boils at 100°C, pure ethanol (ethyl alcohol) boils at 78.5°C, and pure diethyl ether boils at 34.6°C. The vapor pressure curves shown in Figure 5.1 illustrate the variation of the vapor pressure of these liquids with temperature. One can use these curves to predict the boiling point at a reduced pressure. For example, diethyl ether has a vapor pressure of 422 mm Hg at 20°C. If the external pressure were reduced to 422 mm Hg, diethyl ether would boil at 20°C.

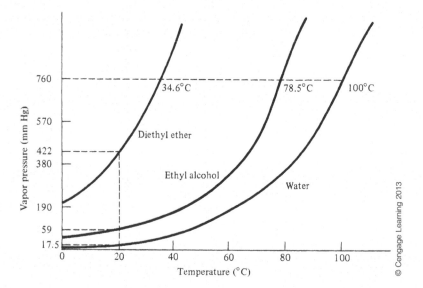

Figure 5.1
Diethyl ether, ethyl alcohol (ethanol), and water vapor pressure curves.

1. To use melting points and boiling points in identifying substances.

2. To use sublimation as a means of purification.

PROCEDURE

**Melting Point
Determination**

1. Unknowns are provided by the instructor. Obtain enough of the unknown to cover the end of your small spatula. Record the code number of the unknown on the Report Sheet **(1)**. Carefully grind the solid into a powder using a mortar and pestle.

2. Obtain a melting-point capillary tube. One end of the tube will be sealed. The tube is packed with solid in the following way:

   Step A Press the open end of the capillary tube vertically into the solid sample (Figure 5.2 A). A small amount of sample will be forced into the open end of the capillary tube. A few millimeters of sample height in the capillary is plenty; there is no need for more.

   Step B Invert the capillary tube so that the closed end is pointing toward the bench top. Gently tap the end of the tube against the laboratory bench top (Figure 5.2 B). Continue tapping until the solid is forced down to the closed end.

   Step C An alternative method for bringing the solid sample to the closed end uses a piece of glass tubing of approximately 20–30

A. Forcing solid into the capillary tube.

Step A

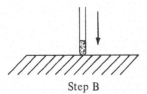

B. Tapping to force down solid.

Step B

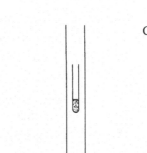

C. Alternative method for bringing the solid down.

Step C

Figure 5.2
Packing a capillary tube.

cm. Hold the capillary tube, closed end down, at the top of the glass tubing, held vertically; let the capillary tube drop through the tubing so that it hits the laboratory bench top. The capillary tube will bounce and bring the solid down. Repeat if necessary (Figure 5.2 C).

3. The melting point will be determined using a commercial device which will be demonstrated by your instructor.

4. Do as many melting-point determinations as your instructor may require. Just remember to use a new melting point capillary tube for each melting point determination. Record the temperature when the solid begins to liquefy **(2)**. Then record the temperature when the solid is completely a liquid **(3)**. Express these readings as a melting point range **(4)**, eg: 80°C–82°C. From the list in Table 5.1, identify your unknown solid by matching your observed melting point range with the compound whose melting point best corresponds **(5)**.

5. Dispose of the solids as directed by your instructor.

**Boiling Point
Determination**

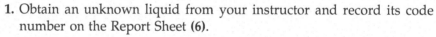

CAUTION

The chemicals used for boiling point determinations are flammable. Be sure all Bunsen burner flames are extinguished before starting this part of the experiment.

1. Obtain an unknown liquid from your instructor and record its code number on the Report Sheet **(6)**.

2. Clamp a clean, dry test tube (100 × 13 mm) onto a ring stand. Add to the test tube approximately 3 mL of the unknown liquid and two small boiling stones. Lower the test tube into a 250-mL beaker that contains 100 mL of water and two boiling stones. Adjust the depth of the test tube so that the unknown liquid is below the water level of the water bath (Figure 5.4).

3. With a thermometer clamp, securely clamp a thermometer and lower it into the test tube through a neoprene adapter. Adjust the thermometer so that it is approximately 1 cm above the surface of the unknown liquid.

Table 5.1 *Melting Points of Selected Solids*

Solid	Melting Point (°C)	Use
Acetamide	82	Plasticizer; stabilizer
Acetanilide	114	Manufacture of other medicinals and dyes
Adipic acid	152	Manufacture of nylon
Benzophenone	48	Manufacture of antihistamines, hypnotics, insecticides
Benzoic acid	122	Preserving foods; antifungal agent
p-Dichlorobenzene	54	Moth repellent; insecticidal fumigant
Stearic acid	70	Suppositories; ointments

© Cengage Learning 2013

Figure 5.3
A Thomas-Hoover Unimelt®.

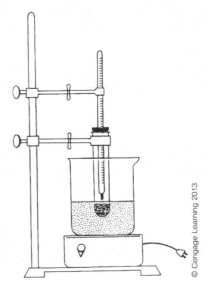

Figure 5.4
*Setup for determining
the boiling point.*

© Cengage Learning 2013

4. Use a piece of aluminum foil to cover the mouth of the test tube. (**Be certain that the test tube mouth has an opening; the system should not be closed.**)

5. Gradually heat the water in the beaker with a hot plate and watch for changes in temperature. As the liquid begins to boil, the temperature above the liquid will rise. When the temperature no longer rises but remains constant, record the temperature to the nearest 0.1°C **(7)**. This is the observed boiling point. From the list in Table 5.2, identify your unknown liquid by matching your observed boiling point with the compound whose boiling point best corresponds **(8)**.

6. Do as many boiling point determinations as required by your instructor.

7. Dispose of the liquid as directed by your instructor.

Table 5.2 *Boiling Points of Selected Liquids*

Liquid	Boiling Point (°C at 1 atm)	Use
Acetone	56	Solvent; paint remover
Cyclohexane	81	Solvent for lacquers and resins
Ethyl acetate	77	Solvent for airplane dopes; artificial fruit essence
Hexane	69	Liquid in thermometers with blue or red dye
Methanol (methyl alcohol)	65	Solvent; radiator antifreeze
1-Propanol	97	Solvent
2-Propanol (isopropyl alcohol)	83	Solvent for shellac; essential oils; body rubs

CHEMICALS AND EQUIPMENT

1. Aluminum foil
2. Boiling stones
3. Bunsen burner
4. Hot plate
5. Commercial melting-point apparatus (if available)
6. Melting-point capillary tubes
7. Rubber rings
8. Thermometer clamp
9. Glass tubing
10. Acetamide
11. Acetanilide
12. Acetone
13. Adipic acid
14. Benzophenone
15. Benzoic acid
16. Cyclohexane
17. *p*-Dichlorobenzene
18. Ethyl acetate
19. Hexane
20. Methanol (methyl alcohol)
21. Naphthalene (pure)
22. 1-Propanol
23. 2-Propanol (isopropyl alcohol)
24. Stearic acid

5 EXPERIMENT 5

Pre-Lab Questions

1. Define *melting point* and *boiling point*.

2. Does the transition of a substance from solid to liquid to gas represent a physical or chemical change? Explain why.

3. What two things happen to the melting point of a solid when an impurity is present?

4. What effect does decreasing the external pressure on a liquid have on the liquid's boiling point?

name _____   section _____   date _____

partner _____   grade _____

5   EXPERIMENT 5

Report Sheet

Melting point determination

	Trial No. 1	*Trial No. 2*
1. Code number of unknown	_____	_____
2. Temperature melting begins	_____ °C	_____ °C
3. Temperature melting ends	_____ °C	_____ °C
4. Melting-point range	_____ °C	_____ °C
5. Identification of unknown	_____	_____

Boiling point determination

6. Unknown number	_____	_____
7. Observed boiling point	_____ °C	_____ °C
8. Identification of unknown	_____	_____

Post-Lab Questions

1. If the external pressure on water is 422 mmHg, will water boil at 100°C, 80°C, or 60°C? Use Figure 5.1 to answer this question.

2. A good sample of benzoic acid melts at 121–122°C. However, a student had a sample that melted over a range, 105–115°C. What did the student conclude about this sample?

3. Boiling points of liquids are all lower in Denver, Colorado than in Detroit, Michigan. Since Denver is in a mountainous region, what can you conclude about atmospheric (external) pressure as you climb higher above sea level?

4. Cocaine is a white solid that melts at 98°C when pure. Sucrose (table sugar) also is a white solid, but it melts at 185–186°C. A forensic chemist working for the New York Police Department has a white solid believed to be cocaine. What can the chemist do to determine quickly whether the sample is pure cocaine, simply table sugar, or a mixture of the two? (A good chemist never tastes any unknown chemical.)

Chemical Properties of Consumer Products

BACKGROUND

Concern for the environment has placed considerable attention on the identification of chemicals that enter our everyday world. Analytical chemistry deals with these concerns in both a quantitative and qualitative sense. In *quantitative analysis*, the concern is for exact amounts of certain known chemicals present in a sample; *Qualitative analysis* is limited to establishing the presence or absence of certain chemicals in detectable amounts in a sample. This experiment will focus on the qualitative determination of inorganic chemicals.

The simplest approach to the detection of inorganic chemicals is to use tests that will identify the ions that make up the inorganic sample. These ions are cations and anions. *Cations* are ions that carry positive charges; Na^+, NH_4^+, Ca^{2+}, Cu^{2+}, and Al^{3+} are representative examples. *Anions* are ions that carry negative charges; Cl^-, HCO_3^-, CO_3^{2-}, SO_4^{2-}, and PO_4^{3-} are examples of this type. Because each ion has unique properties, each will give a characteristic reaction or test result. By examining an aqueous solution of the chemical, qualitative spot tests often will identify the cation and the anion present. The tests used will bring about some chemical change. This change will be seen in the form of a solid precipitate, gas bubbles, or a color change.

This experiment will use chemicals commonly found around the house, so-called consumer chemical products. You may not think of these products as chemicals or refer to them by their inorganic chemical names. Nevertheless, they are chemicals, and simple qualitative analytical techniques can be used to identify the ions found in their makeup.

Table salt, NaCl. Table salt is most commonly used as a flavoring agent. Individuals with high blood pressure (hypertension) are advised to restrict salt intake in order to reduce the amount of sodium ion, Na^+, absorbed. When dissolved in water, table salt releases the sodium cation, Na^+, and the chloride anion, Cl^-. Chloride ion is detected by silver nitrate, $AgNO_3$; a characteristic white precipitate of silver chloride forms.

$$Ag^+(aq) + Cl^-(aq) \rightarrow AgCl(s) \ (\textbf{White precipitate})$$

Sodium ions produce a characteristic bright yellow color in a flame.

Ammonia, NH$_3$. Ammonia is a gas with a strong irritating odor. The gas dissolves readily in water, giving an aqueous ammonia solution; the solution is commonly referred to as ammonium hydroxide. Aqueous ammonia solutions are used as cleaning agents because of their ability to dissolve grease, oils, and waxes. Ammonia solutions are basic and will change moistened red litmus paper to blue. Ammonium salts (e.g., ammonium chloride, NH$_4$Cl) react with strong bases to form ammonia gas.

$$NH_4^+(aq) + OH^-(aq) \rightarrow NH_3(g) + H_2O(l)$$

Baking soda, sodium bicarbonate, NaHCO$_3$. Baking soda, sodium bicarbonate, NaHCO$_3$, acts as an antacid in some commercial products (e.g., Alka Seltzer®) and as a leavening agent, helping to "raise" a cake. When sodium bicarbonate reacts with acids, carbon dioxide, a colorless, odorless gas, is released.

$$HCO_3^-(aq) + H^+(aq) \rightarrow CO_2(g) + H_2O(l)$$

The presence of CO$_2$ can be confirmed with barium hydroxide solution, Ba(OH)$_2$; a white precipitate of barium carbonate results.

$$CO_2(g) + Ba(OH)_2(aq) \rightarrow H_2O(l) + BaCO_3(s) \text{ (White precipitate)}$$

Epsom salt, MgSO$_4$·7H$_2$O. Epsom salt has several uses; it may be taken internally as a laxative or purgative, or it may be used externally as a solution for soaking one's feet. When dissolved in water, Epsom salt releases magnesium cations, Mg^{2+}, and sulfate anions, SO$_4^{2-}$. The magnesium cation may be detected by first treating with a strong base, such as NaOH, and then with the organic dye *p*-nitrobenzene-azoresorcinol. The magnesium hydroxide, Mg(OH)$_2$, which initially forms, combines with the dye to give a blue color. This behavior is specific for the magnesium cation.

$$Mg^{2+}(aq) + 2OH^-(aq) \rightarrow Mg(OH)_2(s) \xrightarrow{\text{dye}} \text{Blue complex}$$

The sulfate anion, SO$_4^{2-}$, reacts with barium chloride, BaCl$_2$, to form a white precipitate of barium sulfate, BaSO$_4$.

$$Ba^{2+}(aq) + SO_4^{2-}(aq) \rightarrow BaSO_4(s) \text{ (White precipitate)}$$

Bleach, sodium hypochlorite, Na. Bleach sold commercially is a dilute solution of sodium hypochlorite, NaOCl, usually 5% in concentration. The active agent is the hypochlorite anion. In solution, OCl$^-$ (hypochlorite ion) behaves exactly the same as free chlorine, Cl$_2$. Free chlorine reacts with I$^-$, from dissolved KI, producing I$_2$.

$$Cl_2(aq) + 2I^-(aq) \rightarrow I_2(aq) + 2Cl^-(aq)$$

The iodine I$_2$ gives a reddish-brown color to water. However, because iodine is more soluble in organic solvents, such as hexane, C$_6$H$_{14}$, the iodine dissolves in the organic solvent. The organic solvent separates from the water, and the iodine colors the organic solvent violet.

Sodium phosphate, Na$_3$PO$_4$. In some communities that use well water for their water supply, dissolved calcium and magnesium salts make the water "hard." Normal soaps do not work well as a result. In order to increase the efficiency of their products, especially in hard water areas, some commercial soap preparations, or detergents, contain sodium phosphate, Na$_3$PO$_4$. The phosphate anion is the active ingredient and keeps the calcium and magnesium ions from interfering with the soap's cleaning action. Other products containing phosphate salts are plant fertilizers; here, ammonium phosphate, $(NH_4)_3PO_4$, serves as the source of phosphorus. The presence of the phosphate anion can be detected with ammonium molybdate, $(NH_4)_2MoO_4$. In acid solution, phosphate anions combine with the molybdate reagent to form a bright yellow precipitate.

$$PO_4^{3-}(aq) + 12MoO_4^{2-}(aq) + 3NH_4^+(aq) + 24H^+(aq) \rightarrow$$
$$(NH_4)_3PO_4(MoO_3)_{12}(s) + 12H_2O(l)$$
(Yellow precipitate)

OBJECTIVES

1. To examine the chemical properties of some common substances found around the house.

2. To use spot tests to learn which inorganic cations and anions are found in these products.

PROCEDURE

CAUTION

Although we are using chemical substances common to our everyday life, conduct this experiment as you would any other. Wear safety glasses; do not taste anything; mix only those substances as directed.

Analysis of Table Salt, NaCl

1. Place a small amount (covering the tip of a small spatula) of table salt in a test tube (100 × 13 mm). Add 1 mL (approx. 20 drops) of distilled water and mix to dissolve. Add 2 drops of 0.1 M $AgNO_3$. Record your observation **(1)**.

2. Take a small spatula and clean the tip by holding it in a Bunsen burner flame until the yellow color disappears. Allow to cool but do not let the tip touch anything. Place a few crystals of table salt on the clean spatula tip and heat in the flame of the Bunsen burner. Record your observation **(2)**.

Analysis of Household Ammonia, NH_3; Ammonium Ion, NH_4^+; and Fertilizer, $(NH_4)_3PO_4$

1. Place 1 mL of household ammonia in a test tube (100 × 13 mm). Hold a piece of dry red litmus paper over the mouth of the test tube (be careful not to touch the glass with the paper). Record your observation (3). Moisten the red litmus paper with distilled water and hold it over the mouth of the test tube. Record your observation **(4)**.

2. Place a small amount (covering the tip of a small spatula) of ammonium chloride, NH_4Cl, in a test tube (100 × 13 mm). Add 0.5 mL (about 10 drops) of 6 M NaOH to the test tube. Hold a moist piece of red litmus inside the mouth of the test tube (be careful not to touch the glass with the paper). Does the litmus change color? If the litmus paper does not change color, gently warm the test tube (**do not boil the solution**). Record your observation **(5)**.

3. Place a small amount (covering the tip of a small spatula) of commercial fertilizer in a test tube (100 × 13 mm). Add 0.5 mL (about 10 drops) of 6 M NaOH to the test tube. Test as above with moist red litmus paper. Record your observation and conclusion (6).

Analysis of Baking Soda, NaHCO₃

1. Place a small amount (covering the tip of a small spatula) of baking soda in a test tube (100 × 13 mm). Dissolve the solid in 1 mL (about 20 drops) of distilled water. Add 5 drops of 6 M H_2SO_4 and tap the test tube to mix. Record your observation (7).

2. We will test the escaping gas for CO_2. Once again, place a small amount (covering the tip of a small spatula) of baking soda in a test tube (100 × 13 mm). Dissolve the solid in 1 mL (about 20 drops) of distilled water. Have 5 drops of 6 M H_2SO_4 ready for use, but do not add it yet. Dip a wire loop into 5% barium hydroxide, $Ba(OH)_2$, solution; a drop should cling to the loop. Now you are ready to add the acid to the test tube. Add the acid to the test tube and then carefully lower the wire loop, with the drop of barium hydroxide on it, down into the mouth of the test tube. Avoid touching the walls and the solution. Record what happens to the drop (8).

Analysis of Epsom Salt, MgSO₄·7H₂0

1. Place a small amount (covering the tip of a small spatula) of Epsom salt into a test tube (100 × 13 mm). Dissolve in 1 mL (about 20 drops) of distilled water. Add 5 drops of 6 M NaOH. Then add 5 drops of the "organic dye" solution (0.01% *p*-nitrobenzene-azoresorcinol). Record your observation (9).

2. Place a small amount (covering the tip of a small spatula) of Epsom salt into a test tube (100 × 13 mm). Dissolve in 1 mL (about 20 drops) of distilled water. Add 2 drops of 1 M $BaCl_2$ solution. Record your observation (10).

Analysis of Bleach, NaOCl

Place a small amount (covering the tip of a small spatula) of potassium iodide, KI, in a test tube (100 × 13 mm). Dissolve in 1 mL (about 20 drops) of distilled water. Add 1 mL of bleach to the solution, followed by 10 drops of hexane, C_6H_{14}. Cork the test tube and shake vigorously. Set aside and allow the layers to separate. Note the color of the upper organic layer and record your observation (11).

Analysis of Sodium Phosphate, Na₃PO₄

Label three clean test tubes (100 × 13 mm) no. 1, no. 2, and no. 3. In test tube no. 1, place 2 mL of 1 M Na_3PO_4; in test tube no. 2, place a small amount (covering the tip of a small spatula) of a detergent; in test tube no. 3, place a small amount (covering the tip of a small spatula) of a fertilizer. Add 2 mL of distilled water to the solids in test tubes no. 2 and no. 3 and mix. Add 6 M HNO_3 dropwise to all three test tubes until the solutions test acid to litmus paper (blue litmus turns red when treated with acid). Mix each solution well and then add 10 drops of the $(NH_4)_2MoO_4$ reagent to each test tube. Warm the test tube in a water bath maintained at 60–70°C. Compare the three solutions and record your observations (12).

1. Bunsen burner
2. Copper wire
3. Litmus paper, blue
4. Litmus paper, red
5. Commercial ammonia solution, NH_3
6. Ammonium chloride, NH_4Cl
7. Commercial baking soda, $NaHCO_3$
8. Commercial bleach, $NaOCl$
9. Detergent, Na_3PO_4
10. Epsom salt, $MgSO_4 \cdot 7H_2O$
11. Garden fertilizer, $(NH_4)_3PO_4$
12. Table salt, $NaCl$
13. Ammonium molybdate reagent, $(NH_4)_2MoO_4$
14. 1 M $BaCl_2$
15. 5% $Ba(OH)_2$
16. 3 M HNO_3
17. 6 M HNO_3
18. Potassium iodide, KI
19. 0.1 M $AgNO_3$
20. 6 M $NaOH$
21. 1 M Na_3PO_4
22. 6 M H_2SO_4
23. 0.01% *p*-nitrobenzene-azoresorcinol ("organic dye" solution)
24. Hexane, C_6H_{14}
25. Test tubes (100 × 13 mm)

name _____

partner _____

section _____

date _____

grade _____

6 **EXPERIMENT 6**

Pre-Lab Questions

1. What's the difference between quantitative and qualitative analysis? Which one are you doing in this experiment?

2. Some Epsom salts are dissolved in water and p-nitrobenzene-azoresorcinol is added. What will happen to the solution?

3. Phosphates are an environmental hazard. What common commercial products often contain phosphates?

4. Below is a list of the materials to be analyzed. Complete the table by providing the name and formula of the salt found in each product, and formula of the cation, and the formula of the anion. The formula for each substance can be found on the chemicals and equipment list.

Product	Salt	Cation	Anion
1. Baking soda (example)	$NaHCO_3$	Na^+	HCO_3^-
2. Bleach			
3. Detergent			
4. Fertilizer			

6 EXPERIMENT 6

Report Sheet

Analysis of table salt, NaCl   Observations

1. $AgNO_3 + NaCl$ _____

2. Color of flame   _____

Analysis of household ammonia, NH_3, and ammonium ions, NH_4^+

3. Color of dry litmus with ammonia fumes   _____

4. Color of wet litmus with ammonia fumes   _____

5. Color of wet litmus with $NH_4Cl + NaOH$ _____

6. Presence of ammonium ions in fertilizer   _____

Analysis of baking soda, $NaHCO_3$

7. $H_2SO_4 + NaHCO_3$ _____

8. Presence of CO_2 gas _____

Analysis of Epsom salt, $MgSO_4 \cdot 7H_2O$

9. Presence of magnesium cation _____

10. Presence of sulfate anion _____

Analysis of bleach, NaOCl

11. Color of hexane layer _____

Analysis of sodium phosphate, Na_3PO_4

12. Presence of phosphate   no. 1 _____

                                        no. 2 _____

                                        no. 3 _____

Post-Lab Questions

1. How could you tell whether a white powder you have is sodium bicarbonate ($NaHCO_3$) or sodium phosphate (Na_3PO_4)?

2. A sample of bottled water was tested with silver nitrate ($AgNO_3$), and it gave a white precipitate. What ion was most likely present, and what chemical would be the most likely source for the ion?

3. A piece of blackboard chalk was dissolved in acid solution and the solution bubbled vigorously. The gas caused barium hydroxide solution to form a white precipitate. What is the gas given off? What is the white precipitate? Write the chemical equation for the formation of the white precipitate.

4. Phosphates are a source of pollutant found in some commercial cleaning agents, and these cleaning agents are banned in many communities. How can an agency test to determine the presence of phosphates in the cleaner?

Determination of the Formula of a Metal Oxide

BACKGROUND

Through the use of chemical symbols and numerical subscripts, the formula of a compound can be written. The simplest formula that may be written is the *empirical formula*. In this formula, the subscripts are in the form of the simplest whole number ratio of the atoms in a molecule or of the ions in a formula unit. The *molecular formula*, however, represents the actual number of atoms in a molecule. For example, although CH_2O represents the empirical formula of the sugar, glucose, $C_6H_{12}O_6$ represents the molecular formula. For water, H_2O, and carbon dioxide, CO_2, the empirical and the molecular formulas are the same. Ionic compounds are generally written as empirical formulas only; for example, common table salt is NaCl.

The formation of a compound from pure components is independent of the source of the material or of the method of preparation. If elements chemically react to form a compound, they always combine in definite proportions by mass. This concept is known as the *Law of Constant Composition*.

If the mass of each element that combines in an experiment is known, then the number of moles of each element can be determined. The empirical formula of the compound formed is the ratio between the number of moles of elements in the compound. This can be illustrated by the following example. If 32.06 g of sulfur is burned in the presence of 32.00 g of oxygen, then 64.06 g of sulfur dioxide results. Thus

$$\frac{32.06 \text{ g S}}{32.06 \text{ g/mole S}} = 1 \text{ mole of sulfur}$$

$$\frac{32.00 \text{ g O}}{16.00 \text{ g/mole O}} = 2 \text{ moles of oxygen}$$

and the mole ratio of sulfur to oxygen is 1 : 2. The empirical formula of sulfur dioxide is SO_2. This also is the molecular formula.

Calculating the percent of sulfur and oxygen from the formula alone can be done to compare with experimental data. The formula used is:

$$\% \text{ mass element} = \frac{\text{moles from the formula} \times \text{atomic mass}}{\text{molar mass of the compound}} \times 100$$

Example 1

For example:

$$\%\,Si = \frac{1 \times 28.09 \text{ g/mol}}{60.09 \text{ g/mol}} \times 100 = 46.75\%$$

$$\%\,O = \frac{2 \times 16.00 \text{ g/mol}}{60.09 \text{ g/mol}} \times 100 = 53.25\%$$

In this experiment, the moderately reactive metal, magnesium, is combined with oxygen. The oxide, magnesium oxide, is formed. The equation for this reaction, based on the known chemical behavior, is

$$2Mg(s) + O_2(g) \xrightarrow{\text{heat}} 2MgO(s)$$

If the mass of the magnesium is known and the mass of the oxide is found in the experiment, the mass of the oxygen in the oxide can be calculated:

mass of magnesium oxide
− mass of magnesium
mass of oxygen

As soon as the masses are known, the moles of each component can be calculated. The moles can then be expressed in a simple whole number ratio and an empirical formula written.

Example 2

When 2.43 g of magnesium was burned in oxygen, 4.03 g of magnesium oxide was produced.

Mass of magnesium oxide $= 4.03$ **g**
− Mass of magnesium $= 2.43$ **g**
Mass of oxygen $= 1.60$ **g**

$$\text{No. of moles of magnesium} = \frac{2.43 \text{ g}}{24.31 \text{ g/mole}} = 0.100 \text{ moles}$$

$$\text{No. of moles of oxygen} = \frac{1.60 \text{ g}}{16.00 \text{ g/mole}} = 0.100 \text{ moles}$$

The molar ratio is $0.100 : 0.100 = 1 : 1$
The empirical formula is Mg_1O_1 or MgO.

$$\%\,Mg = \frac{2.43 \text{ g}}{4.03 \text{ g}} \times 100 = 60.3\%$$

In the present experiment, magnesium metal is heated in air. Air is composed of approximately 78% nitrogen and 21% oxygen. A side reaction occurs between some of the magnesium and the nitrogen gas:

$$3Mg(s) + N_2(g) \xrightarrow{\text{heat}} Mg_3N_2(s)$$

Not all of the magnesium is converted into magnesium oxide; some becomes magnesium nitride. However, the magnesium nitride can be converted to magnesium oxide by the addition of water:

$$Mg_3N_2(s) + 3H_2O(l) \xrightarrow{\text{heat}} 3MgO(s) + 2NH_3(g)$$

As a result, all of the magnesium is transformed into magnesium oxide.

OBJECTIVES

1. To prepare a metal oxide.

2. To verify the empirical formula of a metal oxide.

3. To demonstrate the Law of Constant Composition.

PROCEDURE

CAUTION

A hot crucible can cause severe burns if handled improperly. Be sure to allow the crucible to cool sufficiently before handling. Always handle a hot crucible with crucible tongs.

Cleaning the Crucible

1. Obtain a porcelain crucible and cover. Carefully clean the crucible *in the hood* by adding 10 mL of 6 M HCl to the crucible; allow the crucible to stand for 5 min. with the acid. With crucible tongs, pick up the crucible, discard the HCl, and rinse the crucible with distilled water from a plastic squeeze bottle.

2. Place the crucible in a clay triangle, which is mounted on an iron ring and attached to a ring stand. Be sure the crucible is firmly in place in the triangle. Place the crucible cover on the crucible slightly ajar (Figure 7.1a).

3. Begin to heat the crucible with the aid of a Bunsen burner in order to evaporate water. Increase the heat, and, with the most intense flame (the tip of the inner blue cone), heat the crucible and cover for 5 min.; a cherry red color should appear when the bottom is heated strongly. Remove the flame. With tongs, remove the crucible to a heat-resistant surface and allow the crucible and cover to reach room temperature.

4. When cool, determine the mass of the crucible and cover on your laboratory balance. Record all digits **(1)**. (Be sure to handle them with tongs because fingerprints leave a residue.)

5. Place the crucible and cover in the clay triangle again. Reheat the crucible to the cherry red color for 5 min. Allow the crucible and cover to cool to room temperature. Determine the mass when cool **(2)**. Compare mass **(1)** and mass **(2)**. If the mass differs by more than 0.01 g, heat the crucible and cover again for 5 min. and determine the mass **(3)** when cool. Continue heating, cooling, and weighing until the mass of the crucible and cover are constant to within 0.01 g.

Forming the Oxide

1. Using forceps to handle the magnesium ribbon, obtain a piece approximately 12 cm in length and fold the metal into a loose ball; transfer to the crucible. Determine the mass of the crucible, cover, and magnesium on your laboratory balance **(4)**. Determine the mass of magnesium metal **(5)** by subtraction.

2. Transfer the crucible to the clay triangle; the cover should be slightly ajar (Figure 7.1a).

3. Using a small flame, gently apply heat to the crucible. Should fumes begin to appear, remove the heat and cover the crucible immediately. Again place the cover ajar and continue to gently heat for 10 min.

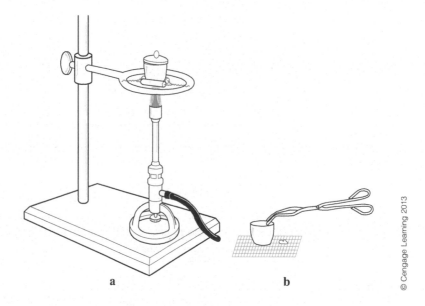

Figure 7.1
(a) Heating the crucible.
(b) Picking up the crucible with crucible tongs.

a   b

© Cengage Learning 2013

(If fumes appear, cover as before.) Remove the flame and allow the assembly to cool for 2 min. With tongs, remove the cover. If the magnesium has been fully oxidized, the contents should be a dull gray. Shiny metal means there is still free metal present. The cover should be replaced as before and the crucible heated for an additional 5 min. Reexamine the metal and continue heating until no shiny metal surfaces are present.

4. When all the metal appears as the dull gray oxide, half-cover the crucible and gently heat with a small Bunsen flame. Over a period of 5 min., gradually adjust the intensity of the flame until it is at its hottest, then heat the crucible to the cherry red color for 5 min.

Completing the Reaction

1. Discontinue heating and allow the crucible assembly to cool to room temperature. Remove the cover and, with a glass rod, *carefully* break up the solid in the crucible. With 0.5 mL (10 drops) of distilled water dispensed from an eye dropper, wash the glass rod, adding the water to the crucible.

2. Set the cover ajar on the crucible and *gently* heat with a small Bunsen flame to evaporate the water. (Be careful to avoid spattering while heating; if spattering occurs, remove the heat and quickly cover the crucible completely.)

3. When all the water has been evaporated, half-cover the crucible and gradually increase to the hottest flame. Heat the crucible and the contents with the hottest flame for 10 min.

4. Allow the crucible assembly to cool to room temperature. Determine the mass of the cool crucible, cover, and magnesium oxide to 0.001 g **(6)**.

5. Return the crucible, cover, and magnesium oxide to the clay triangle. Heat at full heat of the Bunsen flame for 5 min. Allow to cool and then determine the mass of **(7)**. The two masses, **(6)** and **(7)**, must agree to within 0.005 g; if not, the crucible assembly must be heated for 5 min., cooled, and the mass determined again until two successive masses are within 0.005 g.

Calculations

1. Determine the mass of magnesium oxide **(8)** by subtraction.

2. Determine the mass of oxygen **(9)** by subtraction.

3. From the data obtained in the experiment, calculate the empirical formula of magnesium oxide. Use Example 2 in the Background section to see how to write your answers.

CHEMICALS AND EQUIPMENT

1. Clay triangle
2. Porcelain crucible and cover
3. Crucible tongs
4. Magnesium ribbon
5. Eye dropper
6. 6 M HCl

name _____   section _____   date _____

partner _____   grade _____

  EXPERIMENT 7

Pre-Lab Questions

1. What is the name of the formula obtained by writing the subscripts of a molecular formula in the form of the simplest whole number ratio?

2. Below are molecular formulas of selected organic compounds. Write the empirical formula for each:

   a. C_6H_{12} (cyclohexane)

   b. $C_6H_8O_6$ (ascorbic acid)

   c. $C_8H_{10}N_4O_2$ (caffeine)

   d. $C_{16}H_{16}N_2O_2$ (lysergic acid, LSD)

3. A side reaction with nitrogen prevents the magnesium from completely reacting with oxygen in air. What is added to complete the formation of magnesium oxide from the magnesium nitride?

4. Define the Law of Constant Composition. What two elements are being used to demonstrate that law in this experiment?

7 **EXPERIMENT 7**

Report Sheet

1. Mass of crucible and cover after 1st heating   _____ g

2. Mass of crucible and cover after 2nd heating   _____ g

3. Mass of crucible and cover after optional 3rd heating   _____ g

4. Mass of crucible, cover, and Mg   _____ g

5. Mass of Mg metal: (4) − (2) or (3) if used   _____ g

6. Mass of crucible, cover, and oxide   _____ g

7. Mass of crucible, cover, and oxide   _____ g

8. Mass of magnesium oxide: (7) − (2) or (3) if used   _____ g

9. Mass of oxygen: (8) − (5)   _____ g

10. Number of moles of magnesium
    (5)/24.31 g/mole   _____ moles

11. Number of moles of oxygen
    (9)/16.00 g/mole   _____ moles

12. Simplest whole number ratio of Mg atoms
    to O atoms = (10) : (11)   _____ : _____

13. Empirical formula for magnesium oxide   _____

14. % Mg in the oxide from data

    % = [(5)/(8)] × 100   _____ %

15. % Mg calculated from the formula MgO

    % = [24.31 g/40.31 g] × 100   _____ %

16. % Error

    $\% = \dfrac{(15) - (14)}{(15)} \times 100$ _____ %

Post-Lab Questions

1. Discuss how each of the following actions would affect the calculated % oxygen in the magnesium oxide compound. Would the percentage be too high, too low, or remain the same?

   a. The evaporation of water caused "spattering."

   b. Water was not completely removed by evaporation.

2. The white powder often found on objects made of aluminum is aluminum oxide, Al_2O_3. Calculate the molar mass of the aluminum oxide. A 5.00 g strip of aluminum is reacted in air, producing an oxide weighing 9.36 g. Calculate the percent oxygen and aluminum in the compound.

3. Aluminum oxide has the empirical formula of Al_2O_3.

   a. Calculate the % aluminum in Al_2O_3, using the chemical formula.

   b. Calculate the % error for the percent aluminum calculated in question 2.

The Empirical Formula of a Compound: The Law of Constant Composition

BACKGROUND

One of the most important fundamental observations in chemistry is summarized as the **Law of Constant (or Definite) Composition:** any pure chemical compound is made up of two or more elements in the same proportion by mass, no matter where the compound is found. Consider water from your kitchen tap and water from the Pacific Ocean: both are composed of the same elements, hydrogen and oxygen, found in exactly the same proportion—89% oxygen and 11% hydrogen—by mass. We also know that the compound water is composed of 2 atoms of hydrogen and 1 atom of oxygen and has the formula H_2O. If we consider that the mass of oxygen is 16 times the mass of hydrogen, water will always be found to contain 89% oxygen and 11% hydrogen.

We can find the exact percentages for water and verify the above numbers. Using the **molecular formula** (the actual number of atoms in each molecule of a compound), of water, H_2O, the **gram molecular weight** or **molar mass** (the mass in grams of 1 mole of a compound) can be calculated:

$$2\ H = 2 \times 1.008 = 2.016$$
$$1\ O = 1 \times 15.999 = \underline{15.999}$$
$$18.015 = 18.015\ \text{g/mole}$$

The percent composition (by mass), of each element in water can then be calculated:

$$\%H = \frac{2.016}{18.015} \times 100 = 11.19 = 11\%$$

$$\%O = \frac{15.999}{18.015} \times 100 = 88.81 = 89\%$$

These values are constant and are never found in any other proportion!

The **empirical formula** (the simplest whole number ratio of atoms in a compound), is determined experimentally and represents the simplest formula of a compound. For water, the formula, H_2O, is both the empirical and the molecular formula. Some other examples are carbon dioxide gas (CO_2), methane gas (CH_4) and hydrogen chloride gas (HCl). However, for the compound benzene, whose molecular formula is C_6H_6, the empirical formula is CH. Another example is fructose (the sugar found in honey), which has a molecular formula of $C_6H_{12}O_6$ and an empirical formula of CH_2O.

The empirical formula of a compound can be determined in a laboratory experiment by finding the ratio between the number of moles of the elements in the compound. The number of moles of each element can be calculated from the experimental values of the masses in which the elements combine by dividing by their corresponding atomic masses. If the molecular weight and the empirical formula of the compound are known, then the molecular formula of the compound can be determined.

Method

In this experiment we will verify that the empirical formula of copper(II) chloride is $CuCl_2$, and in so doing, demonstrate the Law of Constant Composition. We will do this by reducing a known mass of copper(II) chloride with aluminum to produce elemental copper as seen in reaction (1) below.

$$3\ CuCl_2 + 2\ Al \rightarrow 3\ Cu + 2\ AlCl_3 \qquad (1)$$

A simple subtraction of the mass of Cu obtained from the original mass of $CuCl_2$ will give the mass of Cl. From these masses, the mole ratio of copper to chlorine, the empirical formula, and the percent composition of $CuCl_2$ can then be calculated.

Example

Copper(II) chloride, 5.503 g, is reduced by excess aluminum and gives elemental copper, 2.603 g, according to equation (1). Using this data, the following calculations can be made:

1. Mass of chlorine in $CuCl_2$: (5.503 g $CuCl_2$) − (2.603 g Cu) = 2.900 g Cl.

2. Moles of Cu: (2.603 g Cu) $\times \left(\dfrac{1\ \text{mole Cu}}{63.55\ \text{g Cu}} \right)$ = 0.04100 mole Cu.

3. Moles of Cl: (2.900 g Cl) $\times \left(\dfrac{1\ \text{mole Cl}}{35.45\ \text{g Cl}} \right)$ = 0.08181 mole Cl.

4. Mole ratio of Cu to Cl: 0.04100 : 0.08181.

5. Simplest whole number ratio of Cu to Cl:

$$\frac{0.04100}{0.04100} : \frac{0.08181}{0.04100} = 1 : 2$$

6. The empirical formula for copper(II) chloride is $CuCl_2$.

7. %Cu in sample from data: $\dfrac{2.603\ \text{g}}{5.503\ \text{g}} \times 100 = 47.30\%$.

The theoretical calculated value of %Cu in $CuCl_2$, using the atomic masses, is 47.27%.

© Cengage Learning 2013

OBJECTIVES

1. To calculate the percent composition of an element in a compound.

2. To verify the empirical formula of copper(II) chloride.

3. To illustrate the Law of Constant Composition.

PROCEDURE

Figure 8.1
Suspension of aluminum wire in CuCl₂ solution.

1. On a small weighing dish or a piece of weighing paper, obtain a mass of between 5 and 6 g of $CuCl_2$; record the exact mass on your Report Sheet **(1)**.

2. Transfer the $CuCl_2$ to a 250-mL beaker. Add 60 mL of distilled water and stir the contents with a glass stirring rod until the solid is completely dissolved.

3. Obtain a 45-cm length of aluminum wire. Make a flat coil on one end of the wire, and a handle at the other end. Make the handle long enough so that the wire can be hung over the side of the beaker. The coil must be covered by the solution and should reach the bottom of the beaker (Figure 8.1).

4. As the reaction proceeds, you will see flakes of brown copper accumulating on the wire. Occasionally shake the wire to loosen the copper. The disappearance of the initial blue color of the copper(II) ions indicates that the reaction is complete.

5. Test for the completion of the reaction.

   a. With a clean Pasteur pipet, place 10 drops of the supernatant solution into a clean test tube (100 × 13 mm).

   b. Add 3 drops of 6 M aqueous ammonia to the test tube. If a dark blue solution appears, copper(II) ions are still present, and the solution should be heated to 60°C for 15 minutes on a hot plate.

6. When the supernatant no longer tests for copper(II) ions, the reaction is complete. Shake the aluminum wire so that all the copper clinging to it will fall into the solution. With a wash bottle filled with distilled water, wash the aluminum wire to remove any remaining residual copper. Remove the unreacted aluminum wire from the solution and discard into the solid waste container provided.

7. Set up a vacuum filtration apparatus as shown in Figure 8.2. You may also hook the vacuum flask up to the house vacuum line, if available.

8. Determine the mass of a filter paper that fits into the Büchner funnel to the nearest 0.001 g and record this value on your Report Sheet **(2)**.

9. Moisten the filter paper with distilled water, turn on the water aspirator (or vacuum line), and filter the copper through the Büchner funnel. With a rubber policeman move any residue left in the beaker to the Büchner funnel; then rinse down all the copper in the beaker with water from a wash bottle and transfer to the Büchner funnel. If the filtrate is cloudy, refilter slowly. Finally, wash the copper in the funnel with about 30 mL of acetone (to speed up the drying process). Let the copper remain on the filter paper for 10 min. with the water running to

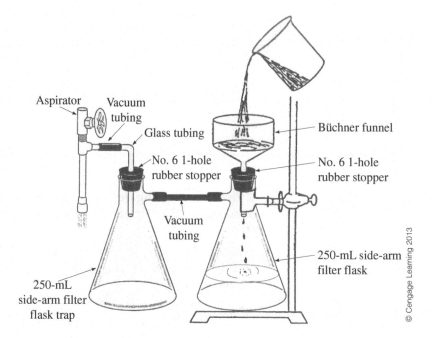

Figure 8.2
Vacuum filtration setup using the Büchner funnel.

further the drying process. The sample may also be placed in a drying oven to complete the drying process.

10. Carefully remove the filter paper from the Büchner funnel so as not to tear the paper or lose any copper. Weigh the filter paper and the copper to the nearest 0.001 g and record on your Report Sheet **(3)**. By subtraction, obtain the mass of the copper **(4)**. From the mass of the copper(II) chloride **(1)** and the mass of the copper **(4)**, the mass of the chlorine can be calculated in the sample by subtraction **(5)**.

11. From the experimental data, determine the empirical formula of copper(II) chloride, and the error in determining the percent of copper.

CHEMICALS AND EQUIPMENT

1. Aluminum wire (no. 18)
2. Acetone
3. 6 M aqueous ammonia, 6 M NH_3
4. Copper(II) chloride
5. Filter paper (Whatman® no. 2, 7.0 cm)
6. Hot plate
7. Rubber policeman
8. Test tube (100 × 13 mm)
9. Pasteur pipets
10. Vacuum filtration setup
11. Wash bottle
12. Weighing paper

8   EXPERIMENT 8

Pre-Lab Questions

1. The molecular formula of methane (often referred to as marsh gas or natural gas), is CH_4. Determine the following for methane: (a) the empirical formula, (b) the percent composition (by mass), of carbon, and (c) the percent composition (by mass), of hydrogen.

2. Calcium chloride, $CaCl_2$, is often used in the winter to deal with ice on walks. Calculate the percent by weight of chloride ion (Cl^-), in the common de-icer. Show your work.

3. Given the following molecular formulas, write the empirical formulas.

Molecular Formula	Empirical Formula
$C_2H_2O_4$ (oxalic acid, found in rhubarb)	_____
$C_2H_4O_2$ (acetic acid, found in vinegar)	_____
$C_4H_8O_2$ (ethyl acetate, found in nail polish remover)	_____
$C_6H_{12}O_6$ (glucose, a common sugar)	_____

COPYRIGHT © 2013 Cengage Learning

8   E X P E R I M E N T   8

Report Sheet

1. Mass of copper(II) chloride: $CuCl_2$ _____ g

2. Mass of filter paper   _____ g

3. Mass of filter paper and copper, Cu   _____ g

4. Mass of Cu: (3) − (2)   _____ g

5. Mass of Cl in sample: (1) − (4)   _____ g

6. Atomic mass of Cu   _____ g/mol

7. Atomic mass of Cl   _____ g/mol

8. Number of moles of Cu atoms in sample: (4)/(6)   _____ moles

9. Number of moles of Cl atoms in sample: (5)/(7)   _____ moles

10. Mole ratio of Cu atoms to Cl atoms: (8) : (9)   _____

11. Simple whole number mole ratio of Cu atoms to Cl atoms   _____

12. Empirical formula for copper(II) chloride   _____

13. Percentage of Cu in sample: $\% = [(4)/(1)] \times 100$ _____ %

14. Actual percentage of Cu in $CuCl_2$:

$$\% = \frac{(6)}{(6) + [2 \times (7)]} \times 100 \qquad\qquad \text{_____ \%}$$

15. Percentage error:

$$\% = \frac{(14) - (13)}{(14)} \times 100 \qquad\qquad \text{_____ \%}$$

Post-Lab Questions

1. What would happen to the mass of copper recorded [see (4) on the Report Sheet] if:

   a. a student did not wait for the blue color to disappear from the solution but continued and collected the precipitated copper by vacuum filtration?

   b. the copper on the filter paper was not dry when a final mass was recorded?

2. If 5.00 g of copper metal reacts with oxygen to produce 5.62 g of 'copper oxide', what is the empirical formula of the 'copper oxide' compound?

3. In an experiment (similar to the one that you performed in lab), a student isolated 6.356 g of pure copper from an initial sample of 9.902 g of a compound that contains only copper and chlorine. Determine the empirical formula of this compound. Be sure to show your work.

4. In an experiment, 3.264 g of pure zinc chloride, $ZnCl_2$, yielded 1.468 g of zinc metal.

   a. How much zinc should be obtained from this amount of zinc chloride?

   b. Calculate the percent recovery of zinc from this sample.

Boyles Law: Relating the Volume and Pressure of a Gas

BACKGROUND

Gases can change the amount of space they occupy, unlike solids and liquids whose volumes are nearly constant. This gaseous property is sometimes called "compressibility" and you can visualize it easily by imagining the differences between filling and handling a water balloon versus an air balloon. (How about a balloon filled with cement?) The way a gas changes its volume under different circumstances is described by a set of rules called the "ideal gas laws." Boyle's Law is one of the ideal gas laws.

Boyle's Law describes how a gas volume is related to its pressure. The pressure is measured as the force of the gas' molecular collisions spread out over the collision area. Pressure increases if the volume the gas occupies decreases. Imagine a piston filled with air; gas molecules are colliding with the walls of the piston as the molecules move randomly inside. Each collision creates a force. All the collisional forces on the walls create pressure. Now push down on the piston, decreasing the volume inside. What happens to the number of collisions? How about the surface area over which the collisions take place? Does the pressure inside the piston increase or decrease?

Boyle's Law Stated Mathematically

You should have concluded that decreasing the volume of the piston increased the pressure inside the piston. Robert Boyle discovered this fact

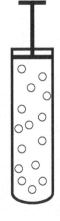 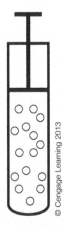

© Cengage Learning 2013

in 1661 and also determined that the change in the volume and pressure had an inversely proportional relationship; as the pressure increases the volume decreases and if the volume increases the pressure must drop proportionately. Two ways of saying this mathematically are:

$$P = k\frac{1}{V} \tag{1}$$

$$PV = k \tag{2}$$

where P is pressure, V is volume, and k is a proportionality constant. In this experiment, you will be illustrating both of these equations; you will prove Eq. (1) by collecting pressure data for a gas at different volumes and Eq. **(2)** by multiplying the pressure and the volume together for several different measurements and seeing that the product is constant within experimental variance.

Often, equations **(1)** and **(2)** are written in a form which allows comparison between two sets of conditions. This equation is commonly used to solve problems involving gases:

$$P_1V_1 = P_2V_2 \tag{3}$$

Example 1

A piston is adjusted to a volume of 45.0 mL and a pressure of 790.0 mmHg. What is the new pressure when the piston is adjusted to a new volume of 35.0 mL?

$$P_1 = 790.0 \text{ mmHg} \quad V_1 = 45.0 \text{ mL}$$
$$P_2 = ? \quad\quad\quad\quad\quad V_2 = 35.0 \text{ mL}$$

Volume decreased, so the pressure should increase. We have to rearrange Eq (3) to solve for P_2. Divide both sides by V_2.

$$\frac{P_1V_1}{V_2} = \frac{P_2 \cancel{V_2}}{\cancel{V_2}}$$

$$P_2 = \frac{P_1V_1}{V_2}, \quad P_2 = \frac{790.0 \text{ mmHg} \times 45.0 \text{ mL}}{35.0 \text{ mL}} = 1020 \text{ mmHg}$$

Demonstrating Boyle's Law

To demonstrate Boyle's Law, you will assemble the apparatus seen in Figure 9.1. The volume of air inside the apparatus can be adjusted by changing the position of the barrel on the plastic syringe attached to the sidearm of the filter flask. By pushing the barrel in, the volume of the air inside the apparatus drops, which increases pressure inside. You'll see the pressure increase because the water at the bottom of the flask will be pushed up into the glass tube by the pressure of the air. The higher the pressure, the higher the water will rise. Pressure will be measured by measuring the height of the water column inside the tube in centimeters. The tube you'll be using is open to the atmosphere; atmospheric pressure pushes on the liquid back down the tube. To make the water rise, the pressure inside the flask has to be greater than the pressure outside. The actual pressure inside can be calculated by adding the height of the water column in the tube to the atmospheric pressure, both expressed in the same units.

The volume of the gas inside the flask must first be determined, and then set by adjusting the syringe volume. The resulting water height will then be measured and adjusted for atmospheric pressure.

EQUIPMENT

500-mL filter flask with plastic tubing

50-cm glass tubing

Rubber stopper without hole

Rubber stopper with hole

30-mL plastic syringe

100-mL graduated cylinder

500-mL graduated cylinder

Barometer

Ring stand with clamp

Meter stick or caliper micrometer

PROCEDURE

1. Obtain filter flask with tubing, a rubber stopper without a hole to fit the top of the flask, and a 500-mL graduated cylinder. To measure the actual volume the flask holds, you must fill it completely with water and then fit the rubber stopper into the top. Put your finger over the rubber tubing and be sure the tubing and side arm are also filled with water. Remove the stopper and carefully pour the water from the filter flask into the 500-mL graduated cylinder. Do not overfill the cylinder; if you have more than 500-mL of water in your flask, pour out 500-mL water from the flask into the graduated cylinder, dump that amount into the sink, and then pour the remaining water from the flask into the cylinder, measuring carefully. Add the two volumes together to get the total volume and record this amount on the report form.

2. Measure 50.0 mL of water with the 100.0 mL graduated cylinder and pour it into the filter flask.

3. The volume air will occupy inside the flask does not include the volume of the water or tube inside the flask, so these volumes must be subtracted out. The volume of the water is 50.0 mL; the volume of the tube will have to be determined. Obtain a glass tube with markings fitted inside a rubber stopper. This should have been adjusted already so that the tube will extend into the water at the bottom of the flask when the stopper is fitted onto the flask. Measure the length of the tube from the bottom of the stopper to the end that reaches into the flask and record the value on the report form. Measure the diameter of the tubing (the caliper micrometer works best for this) and divide the

diameter by two in order to obtain the radius of the tube. Record the radius on the report form and calculate the volume of the tube, treating it as a cylinder. Record the volume on the report form and calculate the volume of the air in the filter flask.

4. Record the atmospheric pressure in the laboratory in centimeters of mercury (cmHg) onto the report form.

5. Assemble the apparatus as pictured in Figure 9.1. Adjust the syringe so the volume reads 30.0 mL. Read the height of the water in the tube in cm and record on the report form. The black markings on the tube are 1 cm apart; there are red markings positioned for every 25.0 cm. You should estimate your readings to the nearest tenth of a cm; if the water level is somewhere inside the stopper, take your best guess at the actual height. Adjust the syringe to a volume of 25.0 mL and read the water height again. Make additional readings for 20.0, 15.0, 10.0, 5.0, and 0.0 mL and record the water heights on the report form.

6. Calculate and record the actual volume occupied by the air for each measurement by adding the volume of the flask to the volume of the syringe at each setting.

7. Convert the height of the water to cm of *mercury*, in order to match the units of atmospheric pressure. Use the density of mercury, 13.6 g/cm^3, and the density of water, 1.0 g/cm^3, to convert to the equivalent height and record this on the report form.

8. Calculate the actual pressure inside the flask by adding the atmospheric pressure to each column height and record.

9. Multiply the pressure and volume readings together for each experimental observation and record.

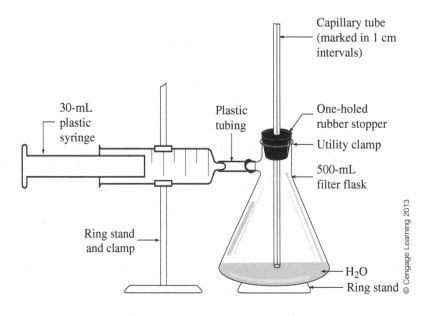

Figure 9.1
Apparatus for studying pressure-volume relationship of a gas.

9   EXPERIMENT 9

Pre-Lab Questions

1. What is pressure? How do gas molecules create pressure?

2. How would the volume be changing (increasing or decreasing) if the pressure were decreasing? Does this demonstrate a direct or inverse proportion?

3. What liquid is used to measure the pressure changes in this experiment and how is it used? How will it change with increasing pressure?

Report Sheet

1. Volume of filter flask   _____ mL

2. Length of tube in flask   _____ cm

3. Radius of tube   _____ cm

4. Volume of tube in flask (V = 3.14 Lr^2)   _____ mL

5. Volume of air in flask (Subtract line 4 from line 1. Then   _____ mL
   subtract another 50.0 mL to account for the volume of water
   in the flask.)

6. Atmospheric pressure   _____ cm Hg

7. Pressure/Volume Data

(a) Syringe Volume (mL)	(b) Total Air Volume (mL) line 5 + column (a)	(c) Column Height (cm H$_2$O)	(d) Column Height (cm Hg) column (c), divide by 13.6	(e) Pressure in Flask (cm Hg) Column (d) + Line6	(f) PV = K Column (e) times Column (b)
30.0					
25.0					
20.0					
15.0					
10.0					
5.0					
0.0					

Post-Lab Questions

1. A student measures a pressure of 775 mmHg for a volume of 565 mL. Calculate the pressure for the same experiment with a volume of 585 mL. See the example in the Background section.

2. A student obtained an average PV value of 42,000 in column (f) of the data table. If the syringe had been able to be adjusted to a volume of 35.0 mL, what would the pressure be inside the flask? Remember that PV = k, and the volume you used includes the flask as well as the syringe.

3. A student performing this experiment notices that the PV values in column (f) gradually get smaller as the experiment continues. Suggest a possible cause for this.

4. After airplane takeoff, most people notice that their ears "pop" as the plane ascends. This is caused by air expanding in volume inside the ear. What happens as the plane gains altitude that explains this effect?

Charles's Law: The Volume–Temperature Relationship of a Gas

BACKGROUND

Jacques Charles observed that for a fixed quantity of gas, the volume at constant pressure changes when temperature changes: the volume increases (V↑) when the temperature increases (T↑); the volume decreases (V↓) when the temperature decreases (T↓). Although first described by Charles in 1787, it was not until 1802 that Joseph Gay-Lussac expressed the relationship mathematically.

Charles's Law states that when the pressure is held constant, the volume of a fixed mass of an ideal gas is in direct proportion to the absolute temperature (expressed in degrees Kelvins). Charles's Law can be written mathematically as follows:

$$\mathbf{V = k \times T} \quad \text{or} \quad \frac{\mathbf{V}}{\mathbf{T}} = \mathbf{k} \tag{1}$$

where V is the volume of the gas, T is the absolute temperature, and k is a constant that depends on the pressure and the amount of gas. The direct relationship is clear by looking at the equations. If a sample of gas at a fixed pressure has its temperature doubled, the volume in turn is doubled. Conversely, decreasing to one-half of the original temperature brings about a decrease to one-half of the original volume.

The law applies, for a given pressure and quantity of gas, at all sets of conditions. Thus for two sets of T and V, the following equations can be written:

$$\frac{\mathbf{V_1}}{\mathbf{T_1}} = \frac{\mathbf{V_2}}{\mathbf{T_2}} \quad \text{or} \quad \mathbf{V_1 T_2 = V_2 T_1} \quad \text{or} \quad \frac{\mathbf{V_1 T_2}}{\mathbf{V_2 T_1}} = 1 \tag{2}$$

where at constant pressure, V_1 and T_1 refer to the set of conditions at the beginning of the experiment, and V_2 and T_2 refer to the set of conditions at the end of the experiment.

Charles's Law can be illustrated by a hot-air balloon. The material that the balloon is made from is stretchable, so the pressure of the air inside is constant. As the air inside is heated (T↑), the volume of the air increases (expands; V↑) and the balloon fills out. With the mass the same but the volume larger, the density decreases (see Experiment 2). Because the air inside is less dense than the air outside, the balloon rises.

This experiment determines the volume of a sample of air when measured at two different temperatures with the pressure held constant and, in doing so, confirm the relationship known as Charles's Law.

OBJECTIVES

1. To measure the volume of a fixed quantity of air as the temperature changes at constant pressure.

2. To verify Charles's Law.

PROCEDURE

1. Use a clean and dry 250-mL Erlenmeyer flask (Flask no. 1). Fit the flask with a prepared stopper assembly, consisting of a no. 6 one-hole rubber stopper with a 5- to 8-cm length of glass tubing inserted through the hole.

2. Mark the position of the bottom of the rubber stopper on Flask no. 1 with a marking pencil. Connect a 2-ft. piece of latex rubber tubing to the glass tubing.

3. Place 300 mL of water and three boiling stones in an 800-mL beaker. Support the beaker on a ring stand using a ring support and wire gauze, and heat the water with a Bunsen burner to boiling (Figure 10.1) (or place the beaker on a hot plate and heat to boiling). Keep the water at a gentle boil. Record the temperature of the boiling water on the Report Sheet **(1)**.

4. Prepare an ice-water bath using a second 800-mL beaker half-filled with a mixture of ice and water. Record the temperature of the bath on the Report Sheet **(3)**. Set aside for use in step 8.

5. Put about 200 mL of water into a second 250-mL Erlenmeyer flask (Flask no. 2) and place the end of the rubber tubing into the water. Make sure that the end of the rubber tubing reaches to the bottom of the flask and stays submerged at all times. (You may wish to hold it in place with a clamp attached to a ring stand.)

6. With a clamp holding the neck of Erlenmeyer Flask no. 1, lower the flask as far as it will go into the boiling water. Secure onto the ring stand (Figure 10.1). Adjust the water level in the beaker to cover as much of the Erlenmeyer flask as possible.

7. Boil gently for 5 min. Air bubbles should emerge from the rubber tubing submerged in Flask no. 2. Add water to the beaker if boiling causes the water level to go down.

8. When bubbles no longer emerge from the end of the submerged tubing (after 5 min.), carefully lift Flask no. 1 from the boiling-water bath and quickly place it into the ice-water bath. Record what you observe happening as Flask no. 1 cools **(2)**. **Be sure to keep the end of the rubber tubing always submerged in the water in Flask no. 2.**

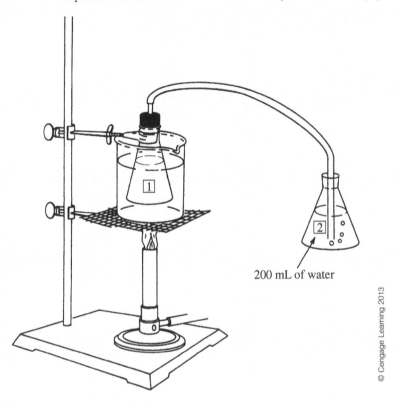

200 mL of water

© Cengage Learning 2013

Figure 10.1
*Equipment to study
Charles's Law.*

CAUTION

The water, the glassware, and the ironware are hot.

9. When no more water is drawn into Flask no. 1, raise the flask until the level of water inside the flask is at the same height as the water in the ice-water bath. Then remove the stopper from Flask no. 1.

10. Using the graduated cylinder, measure the water in Flask no. 1 and record this value on the Report Sheet **(4)**.

11. Determine the volume of Erlenmeyer Flask no. 1 as follows:

   a. First, fill it with water to the level marked by the marking pencil. Insert the stopper with the glass tubing into the flask to be sure the bottom of the stopper touches the water with no air space present. Adjust the water level if necessary.

   b. Remove the stopper and measure the volume of the water in the flask by pouring it into a graduated cylinder. If a 100-mL graduated cylinder is used, it will be necessary to empty and refill it until all the water from Flask no. 1 has been measured.

   c. The *total* volume of water should be measured to the nearest 0.1 mL. Record this value on the Report Sheet **(5)**. The value recorded will also be the volume of the air at the temperature of boiling water. **(6)**

12. Do the calculations [**(8)** & **(9)**] to verify Charles's Law.

CHEMICALS AND EQUIPMENT

1. Boiling stones
2. Bunsen burner (or hot plate)
3. 250-mL Erlenmeyer flasks (2)
4. 800-mL beakers (2)
5. Clamps
6. Glass tubing (6- to 8-cm length; 7-mm OD)
7. Marking pencil
8. One-hole rubber stopper (size no. 6)
9. Ring stand
10. Ring support
11. Rubber tubing (2-ft. length)
12. Thermometer, 110°C
13. Wire gauze

10 EXPERIMENT 10

Pre-Lab Questions

1. What is the mathematical relationship of Charles's Law that Gay-Lussac developed? What do each of these variables represent?

2. In what units must the temperature be expressed in order for Charles's law to work properly?

3. Complete the sentences below for a fixed quantity of gas at constant pressure:

   a. The volume of a gas increases because the temperature _____.

   b. The volume of a gas _____ as the temperature decreases.

   c. The volume of a gas increases by a factor of 4 when the temperature _____.

4. Air in a balloon occupies a volume of 30 L at a temperature of 25°C. What would the temperature need to be, in °C, in order to have the balloon expand to 60 L (pressure is kept constant)? Show all your work using the proper units.

name _____ section _____ date _____

partner _____ grade _____

Report Sheet

1. Temperature, boiling water (T_2) _____ °C   _____ K

2. Observation as Flask no. 1 cools:

3. Temperature, ice water (T_1) _____ °C   _____ K

4. Volume of water sucked into Flask no. 1 (V_w)   _____ mL

5. Volume of Flask no. 1   _____ mL

6. Volume of air at the temperature of boiling water (5)
(V_2)   _____ mL

7. Volume of air at the temperature of ice water (V_1)
($V_1 = V_2 - V_w$)   _____ mL

8. Verify Charles's Law

$$\frac{V_2 \times T_1}{V_1 \times T_2} =$$ _____

9. Percent deviation from Charles's Law

$$\% = \frac{1.00 - (8)}{1.00} \times 100 =$$ _____ %

Post-Lab Questions

1. There are directions in the **Procedure**, which if not followed as written, would introduce errors. Consider the deviations below, and comment on how a student's results would be affected.

   a. A student allowed all the water in the beaker to boil away, but continued the experiment (refer to steps 3 and 7).

   b. Another student was in a hurry and stopped heating, even though bubbles were still emerging from the rubber tubing (refer to step 8).

2. The following data was obtained during a similar experiment to verify Charles's law: (i) Temperature of boiling water (99.0°C), (ii) room temperature (28.0°C), (iii) volume of water drawn into the flask no. 1 (50.0 mL), and (iv) total volume of flask no. 1 (275.5 mL). Using this data, verify Charles's law and determine any percent deviation. Show all work.

3. What would be the volume of an *ideal gas* at absolute zero? What happens to *real gases* before they reach absolute zero?

4. A sample of oxygen gas has a volume of 4.17 L at a temperature of 24.0°C. What temperature (in °C), is needed in order for the volume of the gas to reach 15.0 L?

Water of Hydration

BACKGROUND

Some compounds do not melt when heated but undergo decomposition. In decomposing, the compound can break down irreversibly or reversibly into two or more substances. If it is reversible, recombination leads to reformation of the original material. Hydrates are examples of compounds that do not melt but decompose upon heating. The decomposition products are an anhydrous salt and water. The original hydrate can be regenerated by addition of water to the anhydrous salt.

Hydrates are solid compounds containing water units combined in a definite ratio as an integral part of the crystals. When a hydrate crystallizes from an aqueous solution, water molecules are bound to the metal ion. A characteristic of the metal is the number of water molecules that bind to the metal ion. These water molecules are called *waters of hydration* and are in a definite proportion. Thus when copper (II) sulfate crystallizes from water, the blue salt copper(II) sulfate pentahydrate, $CuSO_4 \cdot 5H_2O$, forms. As indicated by the formula, 5 waters of hydration are bound to the copper(II) ion in copper (II) sulfate. Notice how the formula is written—the waters of hydration are separated from the formula of the salt by a *dot*.

Heat can transform a hydrate into an anhydrous salt. The water can often be seen escaping as steam. For example, the blue crystals of copper (II) sulfate pentahydrate can be changed into a white powder, the anhydrous salt, by heating to approximately 250°C.

$$CuSO_4 \cdot 5H_2O(s) \longrightarrow CuSO_4(s) + 5H_2O(g)$$

Blue 250°C **White**

This process is reversible; adding water to the white anhydrous copper (II) sulfate salt will rehydrate the salt and regenerate the blue pentahydrate. Not all hydrates behave in this way. For example, the waters of hydration that are bound to the iron(III) ion, Fe^{3+}, in the salt iron(III) chloride hexahydrate, $FeCl_3 \cdot 6H_2O$, are held very strongly; intense heat will not drive off the water.

Some anhydrous salts are capable of becoming hydrated upon exposure to the moisture in their surroundings. These salts are called *hygroscopic salts* and can be used as chemical drying agents or *desiccants*. Some salts are such excellent desiccants and are able to absorb so much moisture from their surroundings that they can eventually dissolve themselves! Calcium chloride, $CaCl_2$, is such a salt and is said to be *deliquescent*.

These salts and their hydrates are used in commercial applications. Containers holding pharmaceutical pills often have small packets of desiccant to control moisture so the pills last longer. Unless a desiccant is present, fertilizers will become wet and sticky as they absorb moisture from the air; some will even "turn to liquid" after some time as they absorb so much water that they dissolve. Some humidity indicators use cobalt or copper salts and vary in color as the moisture in the air varies.

Because many hydrates contain water in a stoichiometric quantity, it is possible to determine the molar ratio of water to salt. First, you would determine the weight of the water lost from the hydrate by heating a weighed sample. From the mass of the water lost, you then can calculate the percent of water in the hydrate. From the mass of the water lost you can also determine the number of water molecules in the hydrate salt and thus the molar ratio.

Example 1

Calculating the theoretical percent of water (percent by formula) in Gypsum, $CaSO_4 \cdot 2H_2O$

a. The formula of the compound shows that there are two H_2O units in every single $CaSO_4 \cdot 2H_2O$ unit.

b. Percent of water = (formula mass of 2 H_2O/formula mass of $CaSO_4 \cdot 2H_2O$) × 100

c. Percent of water = (2 × 18.02/172.19) × 100 = 20.93%

Therefore, the theoretical percent of water in Gypsum is 20.93%.

Example 2

A sample of Epsom salt, the hydrate of magnesium sulfate, 5.320 g, lost water on heating; the anhydrous salt, which remained, had a mass of 2.598 g.

a. The mass of the water lost:

Mass of hydrate sample (g)	**5.320 g**
−Mass of the anhydrous salt (g)	**−2.598 g**
Mass of the water lost (g)	**2.722 g**

b. The percent by mass of water:

$$\frac{\text{Mass of water lost (g)}}{\text{Mass of hydrate sample (g)}} \times 100 = \frac{2.722\,g}{5.320\,g} \times 100 = 51.17\%$$

c. The number of moles of water lost:

$$\frac{\text{Mass of water lost (g)}}{\text{MW of water (g/mole)}} = \frac{2.722\,g}{18.02\,g/mole} = 0.1511\ \text{mole}$$

d. The number of moles of $MgSO_4$:

$$\frac{\text{Mass of } MgSO_4 \text{ anhydrous (g)}}{\text{MW of } MgSO_4 \text{ (g/mole)}} = \frac{2.598\,g}{120.4\,g/mole} = 0.02158\ \text{mole}$$

e. The mole ratio of H_2O to anhydrous $MgSO_4$:

$$\frac{\text{Moles of } H_2O}{\text{Moles of } MgSO_4} = \frac{0.1511}{0.02158} = 7$$

Therefore, the formula of the hydrate of magnesium sulfate is $MgSO_4 \cdot 7H_2O$.

1. To learn some properties and characteristics of hydrates.

2. To verify the percent of water in the hydrate of copper sulfate.

3. To verify that the mole ratio of water to salt in the hydrate of copper sulfate is fixed.

PROCEDURE

Properties of Anhydrous CaCl₂

1. Take a small spatula full of anhydrous $CaCl_2$ and place it on a watch glass.

2. Set the watch glass to a side, out of the way, and continue the rest of the experiment. From time to time during the period, examine the solid and record your observations on the report sheet.

3. Did anything happen to the solid $CaCl_2$ by the end of the period? Record your observations on the report sheet.

Composition of a Hydrate

1. Clean your evaporating dish and wash glass with soap and water and dry thoroughly with a paper towel.

2. Weigh the evaporating dish on the laboratory balance; record all digits displayed. **(1)**

3. Add between 3 and 4 g of the hydrate of copper (II) sulfate to the evaporating dish. Weigh on the laboratory balance and record all digits displayed. **(2)**

4. Place the evaporating dish on a hot plate. Cover the dish with your watch glass and apply strong heat for at least fifteen minutes, observing the color of the copper hydrate compound and the appearance of water condensation on the watch glass. Keep heating until there is no visible blue color in the compound and no water droplets on the watch glass, longer than fifteen minutes if necessary.

5. Carefully remove the watch glass from the hot plate with your crucible tongs and then remove the evaporating dish, also with crucible tongs, grasping the dish by the edge. Place the dish on your wire gauze to cool to room temperature. Weigh the dish on the laboratory balance, recording all digits **(4)**

6. Place the evaporating dish back on your hot plate, and cover with the watch glass. Heat an additional five minutes, remove it, cool, and weigh the dish and its contents again. If the mass changes by more than 0.05 g compared to **(4)**, place back on the hot plate for five more minutes and try again. When two successive mass readings agree to within 0.05 g, record it on the report form **(5)**. Turn off hot plate.

7. Determine the weight of the anhydrous copper (II) sulfate **(6)** and the weight of the water lost **(7)**.

8. Carry out the calculations indicated on the Report Sheet to determine the percent water in the hydrate **(8)**, the moles of water in the hydrate **(9)**, the moles of $CuSO_4$ in the hydrate **(10)**, and the mole ratio of water to salt in the hydrate **(11)**. Write the formula of your hydrate in the following form: $CuSO_4 \cdot nH_2O$, where n is **(11)** reported to the nearest whole number **(12)**.

9. Before you discard the white anhydrous salt (as directed by the instructor), add a few drops of water to the salt. What happens **(13)**?

CHEMICALS AND EQUIPMENT

1. Evaporating dish

2. Wash glass

3. Crucible tongs

4. Calcium chloride, $CaCl_2$

5. Copper(II) sulfate pentahydrate, $CuSO_4 \cdot 5H_2O$

name _____   section _____   date _____

partner _____   grade _____

EXPERIMENT 11

Pre-Lab Questions

1. What are hydrates? What are waters of hydration?

2. Why can you use calcium chloride to reduce the moisture in a humid basement area?

3. The formula of Green Vitriol is $FeSO_4 \cdot 7H_2O$.

    a. How many total atoms of all kinds are present?

    b. On heating the hydrate, how many moles of water should be driven off per mole of hydrate?

    c. Calculate the percent of water in the hydrate. Show your work.

    d. If you heat 20.00 g of hydrate and drive off the water, what is the mass of the anhydrous salt remaining? Show your work.

11   EXPERIMENT 11

Report Sheet

Observations on the properties of anhydrous $CaCl_2$

Composition of a hydrate	Trial 1	Trial 2
1. Mass of evaporating dish	_____ g	_____ g
2. Mass of evaporating dish plus sample	_____ g	_____ g
3. Mass of sample (hydrate): (2) − (1)	_____ g	_____ g
4. Mass of evaporating dish plus sample after first heating	_____ g	_____ g
5. Mass of evaporating dish plus sample after second heating	_____ g	_____ g
6. Mass of anhydrous salt: (5) − (1)	_____ g	_____ g
7. Mass of water lost: (3) − (6)	_____ g	_____ g
8. Percent of water in hydrate: % = [(7)/(3)] × 100	_____ %	_____ %
9. Moles of water lost: (7)/18.02 (18.02 is the molar mass of H_2O)	_____ mole	_____ mole
10. Moles of anhydrous $CuSO_4$: (6)/159.61 (159.61 is the molar mass of $CuSO_4$)	_____ mole	_____ mole

11. Moles of water per mole of $CuSO_4$:

(9)/(10)   _____   _____

12. The formula for the hydrated
copper(II) sulfate   _____   _____

13. Observation: water added to the anhydrous copper(II) sulfate:

Post-Lab Questions

1. During the heating of the hydrate, some solid was lost due to "spattering." How would this affect the experimentally determined percent of water in the hydrate?

2. If your sample contained a volatile impurity, what value would be in error, the mass of the anhydrous salt or the mass of the water? Explain your answer.

3. Below are the formulas of some hydrates. What is the mole ratio of salt to water?

Hydrate	Salt	Water
$Na_2SO_4 \cdot 10H_2O$		
$Co(NO_3)_2 \cdot 6H_2O$		
$Mo(NO_3)_2 \cdot 5H_2O$		
$CaSO_4 \cdot 2H_2O$		
$(CaSO_4)_2 \cdot H_2O$		

4. A student worked with a sample of $ZnSO_4 \cdot 7H_2O$.
   a. How many atoms of each kind are present?

   b. What is the stoichiometric ratio of salt to water?

   c. Calculate the percent of water in the hydrate. Show your work.

Solubility and Solutions

BACKGROUND

Most materials encountered in every day life are *mixtures*. This means that more than one component is found together in a system. Think back to your morning breakfast beverage; orange juice, coffee, tea, and milk are examples of mixtures.

Some mixtures have special characteristics. A mixture that is uniform throughout, with no phase boundaries, is called a *homogeneous mixture*. If you were to sample any part of the system, the same components in the same proportions would be found in each sample. The most familiar of these homogeneous mixtures is the liquid *solution*; here a *solute* (either a solid or a liquid) is thoroughly and uniformly dispersed into a *solvent* (a liquid). If the solution were allowed to remain standing, the components would not separate, no matter how much time was allowed to pass.

There are limits as to how much solute may be dispersed or dissolved in a given amount of solvent. This limit is the *solubility* and is defined as the *maximum weight of solute that dissolves in 100 g of a given solvent at a given temperature.* For example, sucrose (or table sugar) is soluble to the extent of 203.9 g per 100 g of water at 20°C. This means that if you have 100 g of water, you can dissolve up to 203.9 g of table sugar, but no more, in that quantity of water at 20°C. If more is added, the extra amount sinks to the bottom undissolved. A solution in this state is referred to as *saturated*. A solution with less than the maximum at the same temperature is called *unsaturated*. Solubility also varies with temperature (Figure 12.1).

Liquids dissolved in liquids similarly may form homogeneous solutions. However, there are liquids that have limited solubility in water. Diethyl ether, $CH_3CH_2OCH_2CH_3$ (an organic liquid), is soluble to the extent of 4 g per 100 g of water at 25°C, and forms a homogenous solution. An excess of the diethyl ether will result in a separation of phases with the less dense organic liquid floating on the water; the result is a heterogeneous mixture. Some liquids mix in all proportions; these liquids are completely *miscible*. The mixture of commercial antifreeze, ethylene glycol, $HOCH_2CH_2OH$, and water, the combination used as a coolant in automobile radiators, is miscible in all proportions and results in a homogeneous solution.

The solubility of a given solute in a particular solvent depends on a number of factors. One generalization for determining solubility is "like dissolves like." This means that the more similar the polarity of a solute is to the polarity of the solvent, the more likely the two will form a homogeneous solution. A polar solvent, such as water, will dissolve a polar compound: an

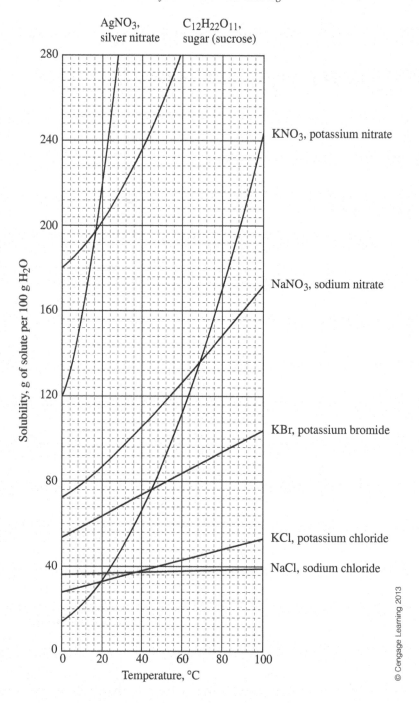

Figure 12.1

The effect of temperature on the solubility of some solutes in water.

ionic salt like common table salt, NaCl, will dissolve in water; a polar covalent solid like table sugar, sucrose, will dissolve in water. Nonpolar solvents such as naphtha or turpentine will dissolve nonpolar material, such as grease or oil. On the other hand, oil and water do not mix because of their different polar characteristics; they are said to be immiscible.

When ionic salts dissolve in water, the individual ions separate. These positively and negatively charged particles in the water medium are mobile and can move from one part of a solution to another. Because of this movement, solutions of ions can conduct electricity. *Electrolytes* are substances that can form ions when dissolved in water and can conduct an electric current. These substances are also capable of conducting an

Table 12.1 *Selected Electrolytes and Nonelectrolytes*

Strong Electrolytes	Weak Electrolytes	Nonelectrolytes
Sodium chloride, NaCl	Acetic acid, CH_3CO_2H (aq)	Methanol, CH_3OH
Sulfuric acid, H_2SO_4 (aq)	Carbonic acid, H_2CO_3 (aq)	Benzene, C_6H_6
Hydrochloric acid, HCl (aq)	Ammonia, NH_3	Acetone, $(CH_3)_2CO$
Sodium hydroxide, NaOH		Sucrose, $C_{12}H_{22}O_{11}$

electric current in the molten state. *Nonelectrolytes* are substances that do not conduct an electric current. Electrolytes may be further characterized as either strong or weak. A strong electrolyte dissociates almost completely when in a water solution; it is a good conductor of electricity. A weak electrolyte has only a small fraction of its particles dissociated into ions in water; it is a poor conductor of electricity. Table 12.1 lists examples of compounds behaving as electrolytes or nonelectrolytes in a water solution.

OBJECTIVES

1. To show how temperature affects solubility.
2. To demonstrate the difference between electrolytes and nonelectrolytes.
3. To show how the nature of the solute and the solvent affects solubility.

PROCEDURE

Saturated Solutions

1. Prepare a warm-water bath. Place 300 mL of water into a 400-mL beaker and heat with a hot plate to 50°C. This water bath will be needed at step 4 and 5.
2. Place 10 mL of distilled water into a 150×25 mm test tube; record the temperature of the water on the Report Sheet **(1)**.
3. While stirring with a glass rod, add solid potassium nitrate, KNO_3, in 2-g portions; keep adding until no more potassium nitrate dissolves. The solution should be saturated. Record the mass of potassium nitrate added **(2)**.
4. Place the test tube into the warm-water bath and keep the temperature at 50°C. Again add to the solution, with stirring, potassium nitrate in 2-g portions until no more potassium nitrate dissolves. Record the mass of potassium nitrate added **(3)**.
5. Slowly heat the solution above 50°C (to no more than 60°C) until all of the solid dissolves. With a test tube holder, remove the test tube from the water bath and set it into a 250-mL beaker (for support) to cool. Observe what happens as the solution cools.
6. When the first crystals appear, record the temperature. Fill a 250-mL beaker with ice and place the test tube into the ice. Observe what happened and offer an explanation for what has taken place **(5)**. (If no crystals have formed, stir the solution with a stirring rod.)

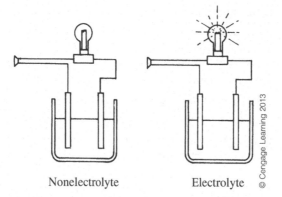

Figure 12.2
Conductivity apparatus.

Nonelectrolyte   Electrolyte   © Cengage Learning 2013

Electrical Conductivity

This part of the experiment can be done in pairs. Obtain and set up a conductivity apparatus (Figure 12.2). It consists of two terminals connected to a light bulb and a plug for connection to a 110-volt electrical wall outlet.

> **CAUTION**
>
> **To avoid a shock, do not touch the terminals when the apparatus is plugged in. Be sure to unplug the apparatus between tests and while rinsing and drying. Do not let the terminals touch each other. When removing the plug from the wall outlet, grasp the plug and pull. Do not pull on the wire.**

The following solutions are to be tested with the conductivity apparatus:
   a. distilled water
   b. tap water
   c. 1 M NaCl
   d. 0.1 M NaCl
   e. 1 M sucrose, $C_{12}H_{22}O_{11}$
   f. 0.1 M sucrose, $C_{12}H_{22}O_{11}$
   g. 1 M HCl
   h. 0.1 M HCl
   i. glacial acetic acid, CH_3CO_2H
   j. 0.1 M acetic acid, CH_3CO_2H

1. For each solution follow steps 2, 3, 4, and 5.
2. Place about 20 mL of the solution to be tested into a 30-mL beaker that has been rinsed with distilled water. A convenient way to rinse the beaker is with a squeezable plastic wash bottle. Direct a stream of water from the wash bottle into the beaker, swirl the water about, and discard the water into the sink.
3. Lower the terminals into the beaker so that the solution covers the terminals. For each test solution, try to keep the same distance between the terminals and the terminals submerged to the same depth.
4. Plug the apparatus into the wall socket. Observe the effect on the light bulb. A solution containing an electrolyte conducts electricity—the circuit is completed and the bulb will light. Strong electrolytes will

give a bright light; weak electrolytes will give a dim light; non-electrolytes will give no light. Note the effect of concentration. Record your observations on the Report Sheet.

5. Between each test, disconnect the conductivity apparatus from the wall socket, raise the terminals from the solution, and rinse the terminals with distilled water from the wash bottle.

Alternatively, the conductivity could be measured using a battery powered conductivity meter obtained from your instructor.

Solubility: Solute and Solvent Characteristics

1. Clean and dry 16 test tubes (100 × 13 mm).

2. Place approximately 0.05 g of the following solids into test tubes numbered as indicated (your instructor will measure exactly 0.05 g of solid as a demonstration; use your spatula to estimate the 0.05-g sample):

   a. No. 1: table salt, NaCl

   b. No. 2: table sugar, sucrose, $C_{12}H_{22}O_{11}$

   c. No. 3: naphthalene, $C_{10}H_8$

   d. No. 4: iodine, I_2

3. Add 4 mL of distilled water to each test tube and shake the mixture (sharp tapping of the test tube with your fingers will agitate the contents enough).

4. Record on the Report Sheet whether the solid dissolved completely (soluble), partially (slightly soluble), or not at all (insoluble).

5. With new sets of labeled test tubes containing the solids listed above, repeat the solubility tests using the solvents ethanol (ethyl alcohol), C_2H_5OH, acetone, $(CH_3)_2CO$, and petroleum ether in place of the water. Record your observations.

6. Discard your solutions in waste containers provided. *Do not discard them into the sink.*

CHEMICALS AND EQUIPMENT

1. Potassium nitrate, KNO_3
2. Sucrose (solid and solutions)
3. NaCl (solid and solutions)
4. Naphthalene
5. Iodine
6. HCl solutions
7. Acetic acid (glacial and solutions)
8. Ethanol (ethyl alcohol)
9. Acetone
10. Petroleum ether
11. Conductivity apparatus
12. Hot plate
13. Wash bottle
14. Beakers, 30 mL
15. Test tubes (150 × 25 mm)
16. Test tubes (100 × 13 mm)

name _____   section _____   date _____

partner _____   grade _____

Pre-Lab Questions

1. Refer to Figure 12.1.

   a. Which nitrate salt (NO_3^-) is the most soluble at all temperatures?

   b. Which halogen salt (Cl^- or Br^-) is the most soluble at all temperatures?

   c. Which potassium salt (K^+) is the least soluble: at (a) 40°C, and (b) 80°C?

   d. Which potassium salt (K^+) is the most soluble: at (a) 40°C, and (b) 80°C?

2. You prepared a solution of coolant for your car's radiator by mixing antifreeze, ethylene glycol, and water. How many phases would you see in the resulting mixture? Is the mixture homogeneous or heterogeneous?

3. A saturated solution of $NaNO_3$ at 20°C has visible undissolved solids remaining. What would you see if the temperature is raised to 40°C?

12   **EXPERIMENT 12**

Report Sheet

Saturated solution

1. Temperature of distilled water   _____ °C

2. Mass of potassium nitrate   _____ g/10 mL

3. Mass of additional potassium nitrate   _____ g

4. Total mass of potassium nitrate: (2) + (3)   _____ g/10 mL at 50°C

5. Observations and explanation

Electrical conductivity

Rate the brightness of the light bulb on a scale from 0 to 5: 0 for no light to 5 for very bright light. (If a battery operated conductivity meter is used simply write down the corresponding number seen on the front of the meter.)

Substance	Observation
Distilled water	_____
Tap water	_____
1 M NaCl	_____
0.1 M NaCl	_____
1 M sucrose	_____
0.1 M sucrose	_____
1 M HCl	_____
0.1 M HCl	_____
Glacial acetic acid	_____
0.1 M acetic acid	_____

COPYRIGHT © 2013 Cengage Learning

Solubility: solute and solvent characteristics

Record the solubility as soluble (s), slightly soluble (ss), or insoluble (i). (A change in color of the solvent would indicate some solubility.)

Solute	Solvent			
	Water	Ethanol	Acetone	Petroleum Ether
Table salt, NaCl				
Table sugar, sucrose				
Naphthalene				
Iodine				

Post-Lab Questions

1. How do you know when a solution is saturated?

2. You found that naphthalene is more soluble in petroleum ether than water. How do you account for this difference in solubility?

3. Solutions of hydrochloric acid caused the light bulb to glow (or caused the conductivity meter to report a higher value), brighter than solutions of acetic acid. How do you account for the difference in behavior between these two compounds?

4. Hexane is an organic solvent that has a density of 0.6603 g/cm^3 at 20°C. If hexane is mixed with water, there is a separation of the two solvents into two layers. Why did this separation occur? Which solvent would be on top?

Classes of Chemical Reactions

BACKGROUND

The Periodic Table shows over 100 elements. The chemical literature describes millions of compounds that are known—some isolated from natural sources, some synthesized by laboratory workers. The combination of chemicals, in the natural environment or the laboratory setting, involves chemical reactions. The change in the way that matter is composed is a *chemical reaction*, a process wherein reactants (or starting materials) are converted into products. The new products often have properties and characteristics that are entirely different from those of the starting materials.

Four ways in which chemical reactions may be classified are combination, decomposition, single replacement (substitution), and double replacement (metathesis).

Two elements reacting to form a compound is a *combination reaction*. This process may be described by the general formula:

$$A + B \rightarrow AB$$

The rusting of iron or the combination of iron and sulfur are good examples.

$$4Fe(s) + 3O_2(g) \rightarrow 2Fe_2O_3(s) \ (rust)$$

$$8Fe(s) + S_8(s) \rightarrow 8FeS(s)$$

Two compounds reacting together as in the example below also is a combination reaction.

$$CaO(s) + CO_2(g) \rightarrow CaCO_3(s)$$

A compound that breaks down into elements or simpler components typifies the *decomposition reaction*. This reaction has the general formula:

$$AB \rightarrow A + B$$

Some examples of this type of reaction are the electrolysis of water into hydrogen and oxygen:

$$2H_2O(l) \rightarrow 2H_2(g) + O_2(g)$$

and the decomposition of potassium iodate into potassium iodide and oxygen:

$$2KIO_3(s) \rightarrow 2KI(s) + 3O_2(g)$$

Table 13.1 *Activity Series of Common Metals*

K	(potassium)	Most active
Na	(sodium)	
Ca	(calcium)	
Mg	(magnesium)	
Al	(aluminum)	
Zn	(zinc)	
Fe	(iron)	Activity increases
Pb	(lead)	
H_2	(hydrogen)	
Cu	(copper)	
Hg	(mercury)	
Ag	(silver)	
Pt	(platinum)	
Au	(gold)	Least active

The replacement of one component in a compound by another describes the *single replacement* (or *substitution*) reaction. This reaction has the general formula:

$$AB + C \rightarrow CB + A$$

Processes that involve oxidation (the loss of electrons) and reduction (the gain of electrons) are typical of these reactions. The use of Table 13.1, the activity series of common metals, enables chemists to predict which oxidation–reduction reactions are possible. A more active metal, one higher in the table, is able to displace a less active metal, one listed lower in the table, from its aqueous salt. Thus aluminum displaces copper from an aqueous solution of copper(II) chloride; but copper will not displace aluminum from an aqueous solution of aluminum chloride.

$$AB + C \rightarrow B + AC$$
$$2Al(s) + 3CuCl_2(aq) \rightarrow 3Cu(s) + 2AlCl_3(aq)$$
$$Cu(s) + AlCl_3(aq) \rightarrow \textbf{No reaction}$$

(*Note that Al is oxidized to Al^{3+} and Cu^{2+} is reduced to Cu. This is because copper is less active than aluminum.*)

Hydrogen may be displaced from water by a very active metal. Alkali metals are particularly reactive with water, and the reaction of sodium with water often produces enough heat to ignite the hydrogen gas released.

$$2Na(s) + 2HOH(l) \rightarrow 2NaOH(aq) + H_2(g) + \textbf{heat}$$

(*Note that Na is oxidized to Na^+ and H^+ is reduced to H_2.*)

Active metals, those above hydrogen in the series, are capable of displacing hydrogen from aqueous mineral acids such as HCl or H_2SO_4; however, metals below hydrogen will not replace hydrogen. Thus, zinc reacts with aqueous solutions of HCl and H_2SO_4 to release hydrogen gas, but copper will not.

$$Zn(s) + 2HCl(aq) \rightarrow ZnCl_2(aq) + H_2(g)$$
$$Cu(s) + H_2SO_4(aq) \rightarrow No\ reaction$$

Two compounds reacting with each other to form two different compounds describes *double replacement* (or *metathesis*). This process has the general formula:

$$AB + CD \rightarrow AD + CB$$

There are two replacements in the sense that A replaces C in CD and C replaces A in AB. This type of reaction generally involves ions that form in solution either from the dissociation of ionic compounds or the ionization of molecular compounds. The reaction of an aqueous solution of silver nitrate with an aqueous solution of sodium chloride is a good example. The products are sodium nitrate and silver chloride. We know a reaction has taken place since the insoluble precipitate silver chloride forms and separates from solution.

$$AB + CD \rightarrow CB + AD$$
$$AgNO_3(aq) + NaCl(aq) \rightarrow NaNO_3(aq) + AgCl(s)\ (White\ precipitate)$$

In general, a double replacement results if one combination of ions leads to a precipitate, a gas, or an unionized or very slightly ionized species such as water.

In all of these reaction classes, it is very often possible to use your physical senses to observe whether a chemical reaction has occurred. Evidence that a reaction has occurred usually includes at least one of the following: formation of a gas, formation of a precipitate (solid), a change in color, or a change in energy which is usually accompanied by a change in temperature.

OBJECTIVES

1. To demonstrate the different types of chemical reactions.

2. To be able to observe whether a chemical reaction has taken place.

3. To use chemical equations to describe a chemical reaction.

PROCEDURE

Combination Reactions

1. In Experiment 7, you reacted magnesium and oxygen to produce a product. Complete and balance that reaction on the Report Sheet and indicate what you observed changing for the magnesium before and after that reaction **(1)**

Decomposition Reactions

1. *Decomposition of ammonium carbonate.* Place 0.5 g of ammonium carbonate into a clean, dry test tube (100 × 13 mm). Gently heat

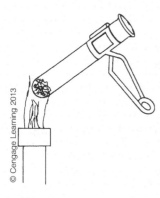

Figure 13.1
Position for holding a test tube in a Bunsen burner flame.

the test tube in the flame of a Bunsen burner (Figure 13.1). As you heat, hold a piece of wet red litmus paper with forceps at the mouth of the test tube. What happens to the solid? Are any gases produced? What happens to the color of the litmus paper? Ammonia (NH_3) gas acts as a base and turns moist red litmus paper blue. Record your observations and complete a balanced equation if you see that a reaction has occurred **(2)**.

CAUTION

When heating the contents of a solid in a test tube, do not point the open end toward anyone.

---

2. *Decomposition of potassium iodate.*

   a. Obtain three clean, dry test tubes (100 × 13 mm). Label them and add 0.5 g of a compound according to the table below.

Test Tube No.	Compound
1	KIO_3
2	KIO_3
3	KI

   b. Heat test tube no. 1 with the hottest part of the flame of the Bunsen burner as shown in Figure 13.2. Keep the test tube holder at the upper end of the test tube all the time. While test tube no. 1 is being heated, thrust a glowing wooden splint about halfway down the test tube (Figure 13.2). (The splint should not be burning but should be glowing with embers after the flame has been blown out. *Do not drop the glowing splint into the hot KIO_3.* Note that the wooden splint is held by forceps.) Oxygen supports combustion. The glowing splint should glow brighter or may burst into flame in the presence of oxygen. Record what happens to the glowing splint **(3)**. Was oxygen produced?

   c. Remove the splint from the test tube. Remove the test tube from the flame and allow to cool. This tube will continue to be used in part e.

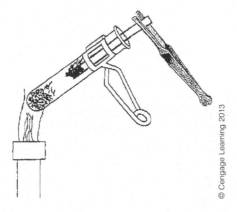

Figure 13.2
Testing for oxygen gas.

d. Add 5 mL of distilled water to test tubes 2 and 3 and mix thoroughly to ensure that the solids are completely dissolved. Add 10 drops of 0.1 M $AgNO_3$ solution to each test tube. Observe what happens to each solution. Record the colors of the precipitates and write complete balanced equations for the reactions taking place in test tube no. 2 and test tube no. 3 **(4)**. (The KIO_3 and KI solids can be distinguished by the test results with $AgNO_3$; AgI is a yellow precipitate; $AgIO_3$ is a white precipitate.) These two reactions are double replacements.

e. Now add 5 mL of distilled water to the cooled test tube 1 and mix thoroughly. Add 10 drops of 0.10 M $AgNO_3$. What color is the resulting precipitate? **(5)** What compound was left in test tube 1 after heating, KI or KIO_3? **(6)**

f. Write a complete balanced equation for the decomposition reaction **(7)**, using your observations from steps c and e.

Single Replacement Reactions

1. In a test tube rack, set up labeled test tubes (100 × 13 mm) numbered from 1 through 9. Place a small piece of metal into each test tube as outlined in the table below. Use forceps to handle the metal. Quickly add 1 mL (approx. 20 drops) of the appropriate solution to the test tubes, again as outlined in the table.

Test Tube No.	Solution	Metal
1	H_2O	Ca
2	H_2O	Mg
3	H_2O	Al
4	3 M HCl	Zn
5	6 M HCl	Pb
6	6 M HCl	Cu
7	0.1 M $NaNO_3$	Al
8	0.1 M $CuCl_2$	Al
9	0.1 M $AgNO_3$	Cu

2. Observe the mixtures over a 20-min. period of time. Note any color changes, any evolution of gases, any formation of precipitates, or any energy changes (hold each test tube in your hand and note whether the solution becomes warmer or colder) that occur during each reaction; record your observations in the appropriate spaces on the Report Sheet **(8, entries 1 to 9)**. Write a complete and balanced equation for each reaction that occurred. For those cases where no reaction took place, write "No Reaction."

3. Dispose of the unreacted metals as directed by your instructor. *Do not discard them into the sink.*

**Double Replacement
Reactions**

1. Each experiment in this part requires mixing equal volumes of two solutions in a test tube (100 × 13 mm). Use about 10 drops of each solution. Record your observation at the time of mixing (**9, entries 1 to 8**). When there appears to be no evidence of a reaction, feel the test tube for an energy change (exothermic or endothermic). The solutions to be mixed are outlined in the table below.

Test Tube No.	Solution No. 1	Solution No. 2
1	0.1 M NaCl	0.1 M KNO_3
2	0.1 M NaCl	0.1 M $AgNO_3$
3	0.1 M Na_2CO_3	3 M HCl
4	3 M NaOH	3 M HCl
5	0.1 M $BaCl_2$	3 M H_2SO_4
6	0.1 M $Pb(NO_3)_2$	0.1 M K_2CrO_4
7	0.1 M $Fe(NO_3)_3$	3 M NaOH
8	0.1 M $Cu(NO_3)_2$	3 M NaOH

2. For those cases where a reaction occurred, write a complete and balanced equation. Indicate precipitates, gases, and color changes. Table 13.2 lists some insoluble salts. For those cases where no reaction took place, write "No Reaction."

3. Discard the solutions as directed by your instructor. *Do not discard them into the sink.*

Table 13.2 *Some Insoluble Salts*

AgCl	Silver chloride (white)
Ag_2CrO_4	Silver chromate (red)
$AgIO_3$	Silver iodate (white)
AgI	Silver iodide (yellow)
$BaSO_4$	Barium sulfate (white)
$Cu(OH)_2$	Copper(II) hydroxide (blue)
$Fe(OH)_3$	Iron(III) hydroxide (red)
$PbCrO_4$	Lead(II) chromate (yellow)
PbI_2	Lead(II) iodide (yellow)
$PbSO_4$	Lead(II) sulfate (white)

CHEMICALS AND EQUIPMENT

1. Ammonium carbonate, $(NH_4)_2CO_3$
2. Potassium iodate, KIO_3
3. Potassium iodide, KI
4. Calcium turnings

5. Magnesium ribbon
6. Mossy zinc
7. Lead shot
8. 3 M HCl
9. 6 M HCl
10. 3 M H_2SO_4
11. 3 M NaOH
12. 0.1 M $AgNO_3$
13. 0.1 M NaCl
14. 0.1 M $NaNO_3$
15. 0.1 M Na_2CO_3
16. 0.1 M KNO_3
17. 0.1 M K_2CrO_4
18. 0.1 M $BaCl_2$
19. 0.1 M $Cu(NO_3)_2$
20. 0.1 M $CuCl_2$
21. 0.1 M $Pb(NO_3)_2$
22. 0.1 M $Fe(NO_3)_3$
23. Test tubes (100 × 13 mm)

13   EXPERIMENT 13

Pre-Lab Questions

1. For each of the reactions below, classify as a combination, decomposition, single replacement, or double replacement.

   a. $2Ca(s) + O_2(g) \rightarrow 2CaO(s)$ _____

   b. $AgNO_3(aq) + KCl(aq) \rightarrow AgCl(s) + KNO_3(aq)$ _____

   c. $Zn(s) + 2HCl(aq) \rightarrow ZnCl_2(aq) + H_2(g)$ _____

   d. $H_2CO_3(aq) \rightarrow CO_2(g) + H_2O(l)$ _____

2. List the following metals from most active to least active. Consult Table 13.1.
   Cu, Zn, Au, Na

3. Oxidation and reduction are usually involved in single replacement reactions. What is gained during reduction and lost during oxidation?

4. List four observations that may be used as evidence of chemical change.

13 **EXPERIMENT 13**

Report Sheet

Write *complete, balanced equations* for all cases in which a reaction takes place. Your observation that a reaction occurred would be by a color change, by the formation of a gas, by the formation of a precipitate, or by releasing heat. In cases showing no evidence of a reaction, write "No Reaction."

Classes of chemical reactions

Combination reactions   *Observation*

1. _____ $Mg(s)$ + _____ $O_2(g) \rightarrow$ _____

Decomposition reactions

2. _____ $(NH_4)_2CO_3(s) \rightarrow$ _____

3. What happens to the glowing splint? What gas was produced.   _____

4. _____ $KIO_3(aq)$ + _____ $AgNO_3(aq) \rightarrow$ _____

   _____ $KI(aq)$ + _____ $AgNO_3(aq) \rightarrow$ _____

5. Color of precipitate produced by remains of test tube 1 mixed with $AgNO_3$ _____

6. The formula of the substance remaining after heating KIO_3 _____

7. _____ $KIO_3(s) \xrightarrow{\text{heat}}$

Single replacement reactions   *Observation*

8. *Test tube number*

    1. _____ Ca(s) + _____ H_2O(l) →   _____

    2. _____ Mg(s) + _____ H_2O(l) →   _____

    3. _____ Al(s) + _____ H_2O(l) →   _____

    4. _____ Zn(s) + _____ HCl(l) →   _____

    5. _____ Pb(s) + _____ HCl(l) →   _____

    6. _____ Cu(s) + _____ HCl(l) →   _____

    7. _____ Al(s) + _____ $NaNO_3$(aq) →   _____

    8. _____ Al(s) + _____ $CuCl_2$(aq) →   _____

    9. _____ Cu(s) + _____ $AgNO_3$(aq) →   _____

Double replacement reactions

9. *Test tube number*

    1. _____ NaCl(aq) + _____ KNO_3(aq) →   _____

    2. _____ NaCl(aq) + _____ $AgNO_3$(aq) →   _____

    3. _____ Na_2CO_3(aq) + _____ HCl(aq) →   _____

    4. _____ NaOH(aq) + _____ HCl(aq) →   _____

    5. _____ $BaCl_2$(aq) + _____ H_2SO_4(aq) →   _____

    6. _____ $Pb(NO_3)_2$(aq) + _____ K_2CrO_4(aq) →   _____

    7. _____ $Fe(NO_3)_3$(aq) + _____ NaOH(aq) →   _____

    8. _____ $Cu(NO_3)_2$(aq) + _____ NaOH(aq) →   _____

Post-Lab Questions

1. Consider the following reactions using Table 13.1. Determine whether a reaction will take place (yes) or not take place (no). Write balanced equations for those reactions that will occur.

   a. $Cu + AlCl_3$

   b. $Ca + FeCl_3$

   c. $Zn + H_2SO_4$

   d. $Zn + PbCl_2$

2. When ammonium carbonate $[(NH_4)_2CO_3]$ decomposes, what gas is produced along with NH_3? Would a glowing splint burn brighter in the presence of this gas? Explain your answer.

3. Your teacher hands you a test tube containing a clear solution with either dissolved Na_2CO_3 or dissolved NaCl. Considering the double-replacement reactions you performed, what one reagent would you add to determine your test tube contents? Describe what you would expect to observe for either Na_2CO_3 or NaCl upon addition of your reagent.

Factors Affecting Reaction Rates

BACKGROUND

Some chemical reactions take place rapidly; others are very slow. For example, antacid neutralizes stomach acid (HCl) rapidly, but hydrogen and oxygen react with each other to form water very slowly. A tank containing a mixture of H_2 and O_2 shows no measurable change even after many years. The study of reaction rates is called *chemical kinetics*. The *rate of reaction* is the change in concentration of a reactant (or product) per unit time. For example, in the reaction shown by equation (1)

$$2HCl(aq) + CaCO_3(s) \rightleftharpoons CaCl_2(aq) + H_2O(l) + CO_2(g) \qquad (1)$$

we monitor the evolution of CO_2, and we find that 4.4 g of carbon dioxide gas was produced in 10 min. Because 4.4 g corresponds to 0.1 moles of CO_2, the rate of the reaction is 0.01 moles CO_2/min. (0.1 mole/ 10 min.). On the other hand, if we monitor the HCl concentration, we may find that at the beginning we had 0.6 M HCl and after 10 min. the concentration of HCl was 0.4 M. This means that we used up 0.2 M HCl in 10 min. Thus the rate of reaction is 0.02 moles HCl/L min. (0.2 M/10 min.). From the above we can see that when describing the rate of reaction, it is not sufficient to give a number. We have to specify the units and also the reactant (or product) we monitored.

In order for a reaction to take place, molecules or ions must first collide. Not every collision yields a reaction. In many collisions, the molecules simply bounce apart without reacting. A collision that results in a reaction is called an *effective collision*. The minimum energy necessary for the reaction to happen is called the *activation energy* (Figure 14.1). In this energy diagram, we see that the rate of reaction depends on this activation energy.

The lower the activation energy, the faster the rate of reaction; the higher the activation energy, the slower the reaction. This is true for both exothermic and endothermic reactions.

A number of factors affect the rates of reactions. Our experiments will demonstrate how these factors affect reaction rates.

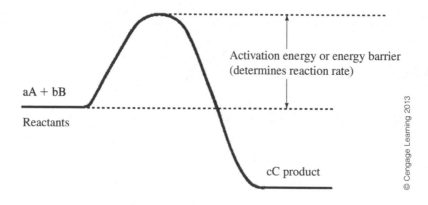

Figure 14.1
Energy diagram for a typical exothermic reaction.

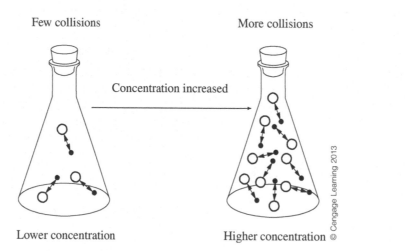

Figure 14.2
Concentration affects the rate of reaction.

1. **Nature of reactants.** Some compounds are more reactive than others. In general, reactions that take place between ions in aqueous solutions are rapid. Reactions between covalent molecules are much slower.

2. **Concentration.** In most reactions, the rate increases when the concentration of either or both reactants is increased. This is understandable on the basis of the collision theory. If we double the concentration of one reactant, it will collide in each second twice as many times with the second reactant as before. Because the rate of reaction depends on the number of effective collisions per second, the rate is doubled (Figure 14.2).

3. **Surface area.** If one of the reactants is a solid, the molecules of the second reactant can collide only with the surface of the solid. Thus the surface area of the solid is in effect its concentration. An increase in the surface area of the solid (by grinding to a powder in a mortar) will increase the rate of reaction.

4. **Temperature.** Increasing the temperature makes the reactants more energetic than before. This means that more molecules will have energy equal to or greater than the activation energy. Thus one expects an increase in the rate of reaction with increasing temperature. As a rule of thumb, every time the temperature goes up by 10°C, the rate of reaction doubles. This rule is far from exact, but it applies to many reactions.

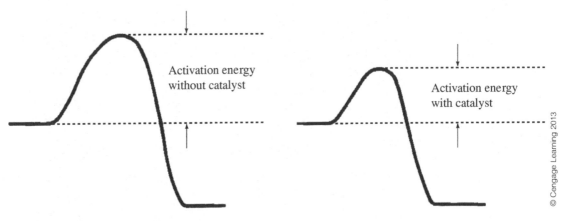

Figure 14.3
Energy diagrams of reactions with and without a catalyst.

5. **Catalyst.** Any substance that increases the rate of reaction without itself being used up in the process is called a *catalyst*. A catalyst increases the rate of reaction by lowering the activation energy (Figure 14.3). Thus many more molecules can cross the energy barrier (activation energy) in the presence of a catalyst than in its absence. Almost all the chemical reactions in our bodies are catalyzed by specific catalysts called enzymes.

OBJECTIVES

1. To investigate the relationship between reaction rate and the nature of reactants.
2. To measure the rate of reaction as a function of concentration.
3. To demonstrate the effect of temperature on the rate of reaction.
4. To investigate the effect of surface area and the effect of a catalyst on the rate of reaction.

PROCEDURE

1. **Nature of reactants.** Do all of the reactions in the five test tubes described below at the same time. Label five test tubes (75 × 10 mm) 1 through 5. Place 1 mL of acid into each test tube as follows: no. 1, 3 M H_2SO_4; no. 2, 6 M HCl; no. 3, 6 M HNO_3; no. 4, 2 M H_3PO_4; and no. 5, 6 M CH_3COOH. Now place into each test tube, as quickly as you can do it, one 1-cm polished strip of magnesium ribbon. The reaction will convert the magnesium ribbon to the corresponding salts with the liberation of hydrogen gas. You can assess the rate of reaction, qualitatively, by observing the speed with which the gas is liberated (bubbling) and/or by noticing the time it takes for the magnesium ribbon to disappear. Assess the rates of reaction; then list, in decreasing order, the rates of reaction of magnesium with the various acids on your Report Sheet **(1)**.

2. Place 1 mL of 6 M HCl in each of three labeled test tubes. Add a 1-cm polished strip of magnesium to the first, zinc to the second, and copper to the third. Do all of the reactions in the three test tubes at the same

time; assess the rates of reaction of the three metals by the speed of evolution of H_2 gas; then list, in decreasing order, the rates of reaction of the metals with the acid on your Report Sheet **(2)**.

3. **Concentration.** The *iodine clock reaction* is a convenient reaction for observing concentration effects. The reaction is between potassium iodate, KIO_3, and sodium bisulfite, $NaHSO_3$; the net ionic reaction is given by the following equation.

$$IO_3^-(aq) + 3HSO_3^-(aq) \rightleftharpoons I^-(aq) + 3SO_4^{2-}(aq) + 3H^+(aq)$$

We can monitor the rate of reaction by the disappearance of the bisulfite. We do so by adding more IO_3^- than HSO_3^- at the start of the reaction. When we have used up all the bisulfite, there is still some iodate left. This will then react with the product iodide, I^-, and results in the formation of I_2.

$$IO_3^-(aq) + 5I^-(aq) + 6H^+(aq) \rightleftharpoons 3I_2(aq) + 3H_2O(l)$$

We can detect the appearance of iodine with the aid of starch indicator; this reagent forms a blue complex with iodine. The time it takes for the blue color to suddenly appear indicates when all the bisulfite was used up in the first reaction. That's why the name: iodine clock. Thus you should measure the time (with a stopwatch, if available) elapsed between mixing the two solutions and the appearance of the blue color. Place the reactants in two separate 150-mL beakers according to the outline in Table 14.1. Use a graduated pipet to measure each reactant and a graduated cylinder to measure the water. Simultaneously pour the two reactants into a third beaker and time the appearance of the blue color. Repeat the experiment with the other two trial concentrations. Record your data on the Report Sheet **(3)**.

Table 14.1 *Reactant Concentration and Rate of Reaction*

	Beaker A			Beaker B	
Trial	0.1 M KIO$_3$	Starch	Water	0.01 M NaHSO$_3$	Water
1	2.0 mL	2 mL	46 mL	5 mL	45 mL
2	4.0 mL	2 mL	44 mL	5 mL	45 mL
3	6.0 mL	2 mL	42 mL	5 mL	45 mL

4. **Surface area.** Using a large mortar and pestle, crush and pulverize about 0.5 g of marble chips. Place the crushed marble chips into one large test tube (150 × 16 mm) and 0.5 g of uncrushed marble chips into another. Add 2 mL of 6 M HCl to each test tube and note the speed of bubbling of the CO_2 gas. Record your data on the Report Sheet **(4)**.

5. **Temperature.** Add 5 mL of 6 M HCl to three clean test tubes (150 × 16 mm). Place the first test tube in an ice bath, the second in a beaker containing warm water (50°C), and the third in a beaker with tap water (20°C). Wait 5 min. To each test tube add a piece of zinc ribbon (1 cm × 0.5 cm × 0.5 mm). Note the time you added the zinc. Finally, note the time when the bubbling of gas stops in each test tube and the zinc

disappears. Record the time of reaction (time of the disappearance of the zinc − the time of the start of the reaction) on your Report Sheet **(5)**.

6. **Catalyst.** Add 2 mL of 3% H_2O_2 solution to each of the two clean test tubes (150 × 16 mm). The evolution of oxygen bubbles will indicate if hydrogen peroxide decomposed. Note if anything happens. Add a few grains of MnO_2 to one of the test tubes. Note the evolution of oxygen, if any. Record your data on the Report Sheet **(6)**.

CHEMICALS AND EQUIPMENT

1. Mortar and pestle
2. 10-mL graduated pipet
3. 5-mL volumetric pipet
4. Magnesium ribbon
5. Zinc ribbon
6. Copper ribbon
7. 3 M H_2SO_4
8. 6 M HCl
9. 6 M HNO_3
10. 2 M H_3PO_4
11. 6 M CH_3COOH
12. 0.1 M KIO_3
13. 0.01 M $NaHSO_3$
14. Starch indicator
15. Marble chips
16. 3% Hydrogen peroxide
17. Manganese dioxide, MnO_2
18. Test tubes (150 × 16 mm)

14   EXPERIMENT 14

Pre-Lab Questions

1. You need to take a medicine orally and want quick action. The medicine is available in the form of a compressed tablet or as a loose powder. Which form would give you the desired quick action? Why?

2. Some reactions require an additional chemical in a non-stoichiometric amount in order to catalyze the reaction. How does a catalyst promote a reaction?

3. Below is an equation that describes the rate of reaction between reagents **A** and **B**:

$$A + B \rightarrow C$$

$$Rate = k \times [A] \times [B]$$

where k is a constant, [**A**] is the concentration of **A** in moles per liter, and [**B**] is the concentration of **B** in moles per liter.

a. What happens to the reaction rate if the concentration of **A** is doubled?

b. What happens to the reaction rate if the concentration of **B** is doubled?

c. What happens to the reaction rate if the concentrations of both **A** and **B** are doubled?

name _____

partner _____

section _____ date _____

grade _____

14 EXPERIMENT 14

Report Sheet

1. Nature of reactants   **Name of the acid**

    Fastest reaction

    _____

    _____

    _____

    _____

    Slowest reaction   _____

2. Nature of reactants   **Name of the metal**

    Fastest reaction

    _____

    _____

    Slowest reaction   _____

3. Effect of concentration

    Trial no.   Time

      1   _____

      2   _____

      3   _____

4. Surface area

    Fast reaction   _____

    Slow reaction   _____

5. Effect of temperature

Trial at	4°C	20°C	50°C
Reaction time	_____	_____	_____

6. Catalyst   **Observation**

    No catalyst   _____

    MnO_2 _____

Post-Lab Questions

1. Is there any evidence from this experiment that would support the notion that the same material in a powder form would react faster than in a lump form?

2. The decomposition of hydrogen peroxide, H_2O_2, yields water and oxygen gas.
   a. Write a balanced equation for this decomposition reaction.

   b. The reaction is fast with the addition of manganese dioxide, MnO_2. Should this chemical appear in the balanced equation? What is the purpose of the manganese dioxide?

3. For the reaction shown in equation (1) in the **Background** section, what should you observe happening to the gas produced
   a. if the concentration of the acid HCl is increased?

   b. if the solid calcium carbonate is in powder form?

4. The temperature of a reaction was increased from 20 to 40°C. You were determining the rate of reaction at each of the two temperatures. The second reaction should be faster by how much? (*Hint:* the temperature was increased by 10°C twice)

The Law of Chemical Equilibrium and Le Chatelier's Principle

BACKGROUND

Two important questions are asked about every chemical reaction: (1) How much product is produced and (2) How fast is it produced? The first question involves chemical equilibrium and the second question belongs to the domain of chemical kinetics. (We dealt with kinetics in Experiment 14.) Some reactions are irreversible and they go to completion (100% yield). When you ignite methane gas in your gas burner in the presence of air (oxygen), methane burns completely and forms carbon dioxide and water.

$$CH_4(g) + 2O_2(g) \rightarrow CO_2(g) + 2H_2O(g)$$

Other reactions do not go to completion. They are reversible. In such cases, the reaction can go in either direction: forward or backward. For example, the reaction

$$Fe^{3+}(aq) + SCN^-(aq) \rightleftharpoons FeSCN^{2+}(aq)$$

is often used to illustrate reversible reactions. This is so because it is easy to observe the progress of the reaction visually. The yellow Fe^{3+} ion reacts with thiocyanate ion to form a deep red complex ion, $FeSCN^{2+}$. This is the forward reaction. At the same time, the complex red ion also decomposes and forms the yellow iron(III) ion and thiocyanate ion. This is the backward (reverse) reaction. At the beginning when we mix iron(III) ion and thiocyanate ion, the rate of the forward reaction is at a maximum. As time goes on, this rate decreases because we have less and less iron(III) ion and thiocyanate ion to react. On the other hand, the rate of the reverse reaction (which began at zero) gradually increases. Eventually, the two rates become equal. When this point is reached, we call the process a *dynamic equilibrium*, or just *equilibrium*. When in equilibrium at a particular temperature, a reaction mixture obeys the *Law of Chemical Equilibrium*. This law imposes a condition on the concentration of reactants and products expressed in the equilibrium constant (K). For the above reaction between iron(III) and thiocyanate ions, the equilibrium expression for the equilibrium constant can be written as

$$K = \frac{[FeSCN^{2+}]}{[Fe^{3+}][SCN^-]}$$

or in general

$$K = \frac{[products]}{[reactants]}$$

The brackets, [ ], indicate concentration, in moles/L, at equilibrium. As the name implies, the *equilibrium constant* is a constant at a set temperature for a particular reaction. Its magnitude tells if a reaction goes to completion or if it is far from completion (reversible reaction). A number much smaller than 1 for K indicates that at equilibrium only a few molecules of products are formed, meaning the mixture consists mainly of reactants. We say that the equilibrium lies far to the left. On the other hand, a completion of a reaction (100% yield) would have a very large number (infinite?) for the equilibrium constant. In this case, obviously, the equilibrium lies far to the right. The above reaction between iron(III) and thiocyanate ions has an equilibrium constant of 207, indicating that the equilibrium lies to the right but does not go to completion. Thus at equilibrium, both reactants and products are present, albeit the products far outnumber the reactants.

The Law of Chemical Equilibrium is based on the constancy of the equilibrium constant. This means that if one disturbs the equilibrium, for example, by adding more reactant molecules, there will be an increase in the number of product molecules in order to maintain the product/reactant ratio unchanged and thus preserve the numerical value of the equilibrium constant. The *Le Chatelier Principle* expresses this as follows: *If an external stress is applied to a system in equilibrium, the system reacts in such a way as to partially relieve the stress.* In our present experiment, we demonstrate the Le Chatelier Principle in two manners: (1) disturbing the equilibrium by changing the concentration of a product or reactant and (2) changing the temperature.

Concentration

1. In the first experiment, we add ammonia to a pale-blue copper(II) sulfate solution. The ionic reaction is

$$Cu(H_2O)_4^{2+}(aq) + 4NH_3(aq) \rightleftharpoons Cu(NH_3)_4^{2+}(aq) + 4H_2O(l)$$
Pale blue   **Colorless**   **(Color?)**

A change in the color indicates the copper–ammonia complex formation. Adding a strong acid, HCl, to this equilibrium causes the ammonia, NH_3, to react with the acid:

$$NH_3(aq) + H^+(aq) \rightleftharpoons NH_4^+(aq)$$

Thus we removed some reactant molecules from the equilibrium mixture. As a result we expect the equilibrium to shift to the left, reforming hydrated copper(II) ions with the reappearance of pale-blue color.

2. In the second reaction, we demonstrate the common ion effect. When we have a mixture of $H_2PO_4^-/HPO_4^{2-}$ solution, the following equilibrium exists:

$$H_2PO_4^-(aq) + H_2O(l) \rightleftharpoons H_3O^+(aq) + HPO_4^{2-}(aq)$$

If we add a few drops of aqueous HCl to the solution, we will have added a common ion, H_3O^+, that already was present in the equilibrium mixture. We expect, on the basis of the Le Chatelier Principle, that the equilibrium will shift to the left. Thus the solution will not become acidic.

3. In the iron(III)–thiocyanate reaction

$$Fe^{3+}(aq) + 3Cl^-(aq) + K^+(aq) + SCN^-(aq) \rightleftharpoons$$

Yellow   Colorless

$$Fe(SCN)^{2+}(aq) + 3Cl^-(aq) + K^+(aq)$$

Red   Colorless

the chloride and potassium ions are spectator ions. Nevertheless, their concentration may also influence the equilibrium. For example, when chloride ions are in excess and in high concentration, a competing reaction takes place and the yellow color of the Fe^{3+} will disappear with the formation of a colorless $FeCl_4^-$ complex

$$Fe^{3+}(aq) + 4Cl^-(aq) \rightleftharpoons FeCl_4^-(aq)$$

Yellow   Colorless

Temperature

1. Most reactions are accompanied by some energy changes. Frequently, the energy is in the form of heat. We talk of endothermic reactions if heat is consumed during the reaction. In endothermic reactions, we can consider heat as one of the reactants. Conversely, heat is evolved in an exothermic reaction, and we can consider heat as one of the products. Therefore, if we heat an equilibrium mixture of an endothermic reaction, it will behave as if we added one of its reactants (heat) and the equilibrium will shift to the right. If we heat the equilibrium mixture of an exothermic reaction, the equilibrium will shift to the left. We will demonstrate the effect of temperature on the reaction:

$$Co(H_2O)_6^{2+}(aq) + 4Cl^-(aq) \rightleftharpoons CoCl_4^{2-}(aq) + 6H_2O(l)$$

Pale rose   Deeper strawberry

You will observe a change in the color depending on whether the equilibrium was established at room temperature or at 100°C (in boiling water). From the color change, you should be able to tell whether the reaction was endothermic or exothermic.

OBJECTIVES

1. To study chemical equilibria.

2. To investigate the effects of (1) changing concentrations and (2) changing temperature in equilibrium reactions.

PROCEDURE

Concentration Effects

1. Place 20 drops (about 1 mL) of 0.1 M $CuSO_4$ solution into a clean and dry test tube (100 × 13 mm). Add (dropwise) 1 M NH_3 solution, mixing the contents after each drop. Continue to add until the color changes. Note the new color and the number of drops of 1 M ammonia added and record it on your Report Sheet **(1)**. To the equilibrium mixture thus obtained, add (dropwise, counting the number of drops added) 1 M HCl solution until the color changes back to pale blue. Report your observations on your Report Sheet **(2)**.

2. Place 2 mL of $H_2PO_4^-$/HPO_4^{2-} solution into a clean and dry test tube (100 × 13 mm). Use red and blue litmus papers and test to see whether the solution is acidic or basic. Record your findings on your Report Sheet **(3)**. Add a drop of 1 M HCl to new pieces of red and blue litmus papers. Record your observation on the Report Sheet **(4)**. Add 1 drop of 1 M HCl solution to the test tube. Mix it and test it with red and blue litmus papers. Record your observation on the Report Sheet **(5)**.

3. Prepare a stock solution by adding 1 mL of 0.1 M iron(III) chloride, $FeCl_3$, and 1 mL of 0.1 M potassium thiocyanate, KSCN, to 50 mL distilled water in a 100-mL beaker. Set up four clean and dry test tubes (100 × 13 mm) and label them nos. 1, 2, 3, and 4. To each test tube add about 2 mL of the stock equilibrium mixture you just prepared. Use the solution in test tube no. 1 as the standard to which you can compare the color of the other solutions. To test tube no. 2, add 10 drops of 0.1 M iron(III) chloride solution; to test tube no. 3, add 10 drops of 0.1 M KSCN solution. To test tube no. 4, add 5 drops of saturated NaCl solution. Observe the color in each test tube and record your observations on the Report Sheet **(6)** and **(7)**.

Temperature Effects

1. Set up two clean and dry test tubes (100 × 13 mm). Label them nos. 1 and 2. Prepare a boiling-water bath by heating a 400-mL beaker containing about 200 mL water to a boil.

CAUTION

⚠

Concentrated HCl is toxic and can cause skin burns. Wear gloves when dispensing. Do not allow skin contact. If you do come into contact with the acid, immediately wash the exposed area with plenty of water for at least 15 min. Do not inhale the HCl vapors. Dispense in the hood.

---

2. Place 5 drops of 1 M $CoCl_2$ solution in test tube no. 1. Add concentrated HCl dropwise until a color change occurs. Record your observation on the Report Sheet **(8)**.

3. Place 1 mL $CoCl_2$ solution in test tube no. 2. Note the color. Immerse the test tube into the boiling-water bath. Report your observations on the Report Sheet **(9)** and **(10)**.

CHEMICALS AND EQUIPMENT

1. 0.1 M $CuSO_4$
2. 1 M NH_3
3. 1 M HCl
4. Saturated NaCl
5. Concentrated HCl
6. 0.1 M KSCN
7. 0.1 M $FeCl_3$
8. 1 M $CoCl_2$
9. $H_2PO_4^-$/HPO_4^{2-} solution
10. Litmus paper
11. Test tubes (100 × 13 mm)

| 15 | **E X P E R I M E N T   1 5** |

Pre-Lab Questions

1. For the reaction at 20°C,

   $$NH_3(aq) + H^+(aq) \rightleftharpoons NH_4^+(aq)$$

   the equilibrium constant is calculated to be $K = 4.5 \times 10^8$.

   a.   Write the equilibrium expression for this reaction.

   b.   From the size of the number for K, does the equilibrium lie to the left or to the right?

2. If the reaction between iron(III) ion and thiocyanate ion,

   $$Fe^{3+}(aq) + SCN^-(aq) \rightleftharpoons FeSCN^{2+}(aq),$$

   yielded an equilibrium concentration of 0.30 M for Fe^{3+} and 0.30 M for SCN^-, what is the equilibrium concentration of the red iron(III)-thiocyanate complex? ($K_{eq} = 207$) Show your work.

3. In the reaction below,

   $$NH_3(g) + H_2O(l) \rightleftharpoons NH_2^- + H_3O^+$$

   the equilibrium constant is 10^{-34}. Is this reaction likely to take place? Explain your answer.

name _____ section _____ date _____

partner _____ grade _____

15   **E X P E R I M E N T   1 5**

Report Sheet

1. What is the color of the copper–ammonia complex? _____

   How many drops of 1 M ammonia did you add
   to cause a change in color? _____

2. How many drops of 1 M HCl did you add to cause
   a change in color back to pale blue? _____

3. Testing the phosphate solution, what was the color
   of the red litmus paper? _____

   What was the color of the blue litmus paper? _____

4. Testing the 1 M HCl solution, what was the color
   of the red litmus paper? _____

   What was the color of the blue litmus paper? _____

5. After adding 1 drop of 1 M HCl to the phosphate
   solution and testing it with litmus paper, what was
   the color of the red litmus paper? _____

   What was the color of the blue litmus paper? _____

   Was your phosphate solution acidic, basic, or neutral

   a. before the addition of HCl? _____

   b. after the addition of HCl? _____

   Was your solution after adding HCl acidic, basic, or neutral? _____

6. Compare the colors in each of the test tubes containing
   the iron(III) chloride–thiocyanate mixtures:

   no. 1 _____

   no. 2 _____

   no. 3 _____

   no. 4 _____

7. In which direction did the equilibrium shift in test tube

    no. 2   _____

    no. 3   _____

    no. 4   _____

8. What is the color of the $CoCl_2$ solution

    a. before the addition of HCl?   _____

    b. after the addition of HCl?   _____

9. What is the color of the $CoCl_2$ solution

    a. at room temperature?   _____

    b. at boiling water temperature?   _____

10. In which direction did the equilibrium shift
upon heating?   _____

11. From the above shift, determine if the reaction
was exothermic or endothermic.   _____

Post-Lab Questions

1. The reaction below competes with the formation of the $FeSCN^{2+}$ complex:

$$Fe^{3+}(aq) + 4Cl^-(aq) \rightleftharpoons FeCl_4^-(aq)$$
$$\text{yellow} \qquad\qquad\qquad \text{colorless}$$

Explain what would happen to the color of a dilute solution containing $FeCl_4^-$ if

a. you added a solution containing silver ion, Ag^+. (Silver ion reacts with chloride ion in solution to form the precipitate AgCl.)

b. you added a solution of sodium chloride, NaCl.

c. you added concentrated HCl.

2. The Haber process is an important reaction for the fixation of nitrogen; nitrogen is converted into ammonia, an important component in the production of fertilizers.

$$N_2(g) + 3H_2(g) \rightleftharpoons 2NH_3(g) + 22{,}000 \text{ cal.}$$

Consider the reaction is at equilibrium. Explain in which direction (left, right) the equilibrium is shifted when

a. more nitrogen is added?

b. more hydrogen is added?

c. ammonia is removed?

d. the reaction is cooled?

pH and Buffer Solutions

BACKGROUND

We frequently encounter acids and bases in our daily life. Fruits, such as oranges and apples, contain acids. Household ammonia, a cleaning agent, and Liquid Plumber® are bases. *Acids* are compounds that can donate a proton (hydrogen ion). *Bases* are compounds that can accept a proton. This classification system was proposed simultaneously by Johannes Brønsted and Thomas Lowry in 1923, and it is known as the Brønsted-Lowry theory. Thus any proton donor is an acid, and any proton acceptor is a base.

When HCl reacts with water

$$HCl + H_2O \rightleftharpoons H_3O^+ + Cl^-$$

HCl is an **acid** and H_2O is a **base** because HCl **donated a proton,** thereby becoming Cl^-, and water **accepted a proton,** thereby becoming H_3O^+ (hydronium ion).

In the reverse reaction (from right to left) the H_3O^+ is an acid and the Cl^- is a base. As the arrow indicates, the equilibrium in this reaction lies far to the right. That is, out of every 1000 HCl molecules dissolved in water, 990 are converted to Cl^- and only 10 remain in the form of HCl at equilibrium. But H_3O^+ is also an acid and can donate a proton to the base, Cl^-. Why do hydronium ions not give up protons to Cl^- with equal ease and form more HCl? This is because different acids and bases have different strengths. HCl is a stronger acid than hydronium ion, and water is a stronger base than Cl^-.

In the Brønsted-Lowry theory, every acid–base reaction creates its *conjugate acid–base pair*. In the above reaction HCl is an acid, which, after giving up a proton, becomes a conjugate base, Cl^-. Similarly, water is a base, which, after accepting a proton, becomes a conjugate acid, the hydronium ion.

Conjugate base–acid pair

$$HCl + H_2O \rightleftharpoons H_3O^+ + Cl^-$$

Conjugate acid–base pair

Some acids can give up only one proton. These are *monoprotic* acids. Examples are ⒣Cl, ⒣NO₃, HCOO⒣, and CH₃COO⒣. The hydrogens circled are the ones donated. Other acids yield two or three protons. These are called *diprotic* or *triprotic* acids, respectively. Examples of diprotic acids are H_2SO_4 and H_2CO_3; an example of a triprotic acid is H_3PO_4. However, in the Brønsted-Lowry theory, each acid is considered monoprotic, and a diprotic acid (such as carbonic acid) donates its protons in two distinct steps:

1. $H_2CO_3 + H_2O \rightleftharpoons H_3O^+ + HCO_3^-$

2. $HCO_3^- + H_2O \rightleftharpoons H_3O^+ + CO_3^{2-}$

Thus the compound HCO_3^- is a conjugate base in the first reaction and an acid in the second reaction. A compound that can act either as an acid or a base is called *amphiprotic*.

In the self-ionization reaction of water,

$$H_2O + H_2O \rightleftharpoons H_3O^+ + OH^-$$

one water acts as an acid (proton donor) and the other as a base (proton acceptor). In pure water, the equilibrium lies far to the left, that is, only very few hydronium and hydroxyl ions are formed. In fact, only 1.00×10^{-7} moles of hydronium ion and 1.00×10^{-7} moles of hydroxide ion are found in 1 L of water. The dissociation constant for the self-ionization of water is

$$K_d = \frac{[H_3O^+][OH^-]}{[H_2O]^2}$$

This can be rewritten as

$$K_w = K_d[H_2O]^2 = [H_3O^+][OH^-]$$

K_w, the **ion product of water,** is still a constant because very few water molecules reacted to yield hydronium and hydroxide ions; hence the concentration of water essentially remained constant. At room temperature,

$$K_w = 1.00 \times 10^{-14} = [1.00 \times 10^{-7}] \times [1.00 \times 10^{-7}]$$

This value of the ion product of water applies not only to pure water but to any aqueous (water) solution. This is very convenient because if we know the concentration of the hydronium ion, we automatically know the concentration of the hydroxide ion, and vice versa. For example, if in a 0.01 M HCl solution, HCl dissociates completely, the hydronium ion concentration is $[H_3O^+] = 1.00 \times 10^{-2}$ M. This means that the $[OH^-]$ is

$$[OH^-] = \frac{K_w}{[H_3O^+]} = \frac{1.00 \times 10^{-14}}{1.00 \times 10^{-2}} = 1.00 \times 10^{-12} \text{ M}$$

To measure the strength of an aqueous acidic or basic solution, P. L. Sorensen introduced the pH scale.

$$pH = -\log[H_3O^+]$$

In pure water, we have seen that the hydronium ion concentration is 1.00×10^{-7} M. The logarithm of this is -7; thus, the pH of pure water is 7. Because water is an amphiprotic compound, pH 7 means a neutral solution. On the other hand, in a 0.01 M HCl solution (dissociating completely), we have $[H_3O^+] = 1.00 \times 10^{-2}$ M. Thus its pH is 2. The pH scale shows that acidic solutions have a pH less than 7 and basic solutions have a pH greater than 7.

pH 0 1 2 3 4 5 6 7 8 9 10 11 12 13 14

acidic   neutral   basic

The pH of a solution can be measured conveniently by special instruments called pH meters. All that must be done is to insert the electrodes of the pH meter into the solution to be measured and read the pH from a scale. The pH of a solution can also be obtained, although less precisely, by using a pH indicator paper. The paper is impregnated with organic compounds that change their color at different pH values. The color shown by the paper is then compared with a color chart provided by the manufacturer.

There are certain solutions that resist a change in the pH even when we add to them acids or bases. Such systems are called *buffers*. A mixture of a weak acid and its conjugate base usually forms a good buffer system. An example is carbonic acid, the most important buffer in our blood, which maintains the pH close to 7.4. Buffers resist large changes in pH because of the Le Chatelier Principle governing equilibrium conditions. In the carbonic acid–bicarbonate (weak acid–conjugate base) buffer system,

$$H_2CO_3 + H_2O \rightleftharpoons HCO_3^- + H_3O^+$$

any addition of an acid, H_3O^+, will shift the equilibrium to the left. Thus this reduces the hydronium ion concentration, returning it to the initial value so that it stays constant; hence the change in pH is small. If a base, OH^-, is added to such a buffer system, it will react with the H_3O^+ of the buffer. But the equilibrium then shifts to the right, replacing the reacted hydronium ions; hence again, the change in pH is small.

Buffers stabilize a solution at a certain pH. This depends on the nature of the buffer and its concentration. For example, the carbonic acid–bicarbonate system has a pH of 6.37 when the two ingredients are at equimolar concentration. A change in the concentration of the carbonic acid relative to its conjugate base can shift the pH of the buffer. The Henderson-Hasselbalch equation below gives the relationship between pH and concentration.

$$pH = pK_a + \log \frac{[A^-]}{[HA]}$$

In this equation the pK_a is $-\log K_a$, where K_a is the dissociation constant of carbonic acid,

$$K_a = \frac{[HCO_3^-][H_3O^+]}{[H_2CO_3]}$$

[HA] is the concentration of the acid, and $[A^-]$ is the concentration of the conjugate base. The pK_a of the carbonic acid–bicarbonate system is 6.37. When equimolar conditions exist, then $[HA] = [A^-]$. In this case, the second term in the Henderson-Hasselbalch equation is zero. This is so because $[A^-]/[HA] = 1$, and $\log 1 = 0$. Thus at equimolar concentration of the acid–conjugate base, the pH of the buffer equals the pK_a; in the carbonic acid–bicarbonate system this is 6.37. If, however, we have ten times more bicarbonate than carbonic acid, $[A^-]/[HA] = 10$, then $\log 10 = 1$ and the pH of the buffer will be

$$pH = pK_a + \frac{\log [A^-]}{[HA]} = 6.37 + 1.0 = 7.37$$

This is what happens in our blood—the bicarbonate concentration is 10 times that of the carbonic acid and this keeps our blood at a pH of 7.4. Any large change in the pH of our blood may be fatal (acidosis or alkalosis). Other buffer systems work the same way. For example, the second buffer system in our blood is

$$H_2PO_4^- + H_2O \rightleftharpoons HPO_4^{2-} + H_3O^+$$

The pK_a of this buffer system is 7.21. It requires a 1.6:1.0 molar ratio of HPO_4^{2-} to $H_2PO_4^-$ to maintain our blood at pH 7.4.

OBJECTIVES

1. To learn how to measure the pH of a solution.
2. To understand the operation of buffer systems.

PROCEDURE

Measurement of pH

1. Add 1 drop of 0.1 M HCl to the first depression of a spot plate. Dip a 2-cm-long universal pH paper into the solution. Remove the excess liquid from the paper by touching the plate. Compare the color of the paper to the color chart provided (Figure 16.1). Record the pH on your Report Sheet **(1)**.

2. Repeat the same procedure with 0.1 M acetic acid, 0.1 M sodium acetate, 0.1 M carbonic acid (or club soda or seltzer), 0.1 M sodium bicarbonate, 0.1 M ammonia, and 0.1 M NaOH. For each solution, use a different depression of the spot plate and a new piece of pH paper. Record your results on the Report Sheet **(1)**.

3. Depending on the availability of the number of pH meters, this may be a class exercise (demonstration), or 2–4 students may use one pH meter. Add 5 mL of 0.1 M acetic acid to a dry and clean 10-mL beaker. Wash the electrode over a 200-mL beaker with distilled or deionized water contained in a wash bottle. The 200-mL beaker serves to collect the wash water. Gently wipe the electrode with Kimwipes® (or other soft tissues) to dryness. Insert the dry electrode into the acetic acid solution. Your pH meter has been calibrated by your instructor. Switch "on" the pH meter and read the pH from the position of the needle on

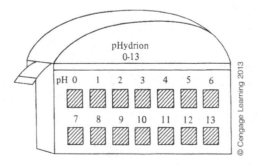

Figure 16.1
pH paper dispenser.

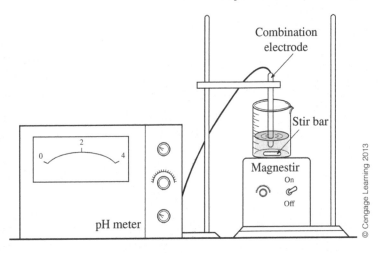

Combination
electrode

Stir bar

Magnestir
On
Off

pH meter

© Cengage Learning 2013

Figure 16.2
pH meter.

your scale. Alternatively, if you have a digital pH meter, a number corresponding to the pH will appear (Figure 16.2).

CAUTION

Make sure the electrode is immersed into the solution but does not touch the walls or the bottom of the beaker. Electrodes are made of thin glass, and they break easily if you don't handle them gently.

4. Repeat the same procedures with 0.1 M sodium acetate, 0.1 M carbonic acid, 0.1 M sodium bicarbonate, and 0.1 M ammonia. Make certain that for each solution you use a dry and clean beaker, and before each measurement wash the electrode with distilled water and dry with Kimwipes®. Record your data on the Report Sheet **(2)**.

Buffer Systems

5. Prepare four buffer systems in four separate, labeled, dry, and clean 50-mL beakers, as follows:

   a. 5 mL 0.1 M acetic acid + 5 mL 0.1 M sodium acetate

   b. 1 mL 0.1 M acetic acid + 10 mL 0.1 M sodium acetate

   c. 5 mL 0.1 M carbonic acid + 5 mL 0.1 M sodium bicarbonate

   d. 1 mL 0.1 M carbonic acid + 10 mL 0.1 M sodium bicarbonate

   Measure the pH of each buffer system with the aid of a pH meter. Record your data on the Report Sheet **(3)**, **(6)**, **(9)**, and **(12)**.

6. Divide each of the buffers you prepared (from above: a, b, c, d) into two halves (5 mL each) and place them into clean and dry 10-mL beakers.

   a. To the first 5-mL sample of buffer (a), add 0.5 mL of 0.1 M HCl. Mix and measure the pH with the aid of a pH meter. Record your data on the Report Sheet **(4)**.

   b. To the second 5-mL sample of buffer (a), add 0.5 mL of 0.1 M NaOH. Mix and measure the pH with a pH meter. Record your data on the Report Sheet **(5)**.

7. Repeat the same measurements, following the steps in **6a** and **6b**, using buffers (b), (c), and (d). Be sure to use clean, dry 10-mL beakers for

each preparation. Record your data on the Report Sheet for the appropriate buffer system at the spaces **(7)**, **(8)**, **(10)**, **(11)**, **(13)**, and **(14)**.

8. Place 5 mL of distilled water in each of two 10-mL beakers. Measure the pH of distilled water with a pH meter. Record the result on the Report Sheet **(15)**.

   a. To the first sample of distilled water, add 0.5 mL of 0.1 M HCl. Mix and measure the pH with a pH meter. Record the result on the Report Sheet **(16)**.

   b. To the second sample of distilled water, add 0.1 M NaOH. Mix and measure the pH as before. Record the result on the Report Sheet **(17)**.

9. Dispose of all solutions in properly labeled liquid waste containers.

CHEMICALS AND EQUIPMENT

1. pH meter
2. pH paper, universal
3. Kimwipes®
4. Wash bottle
5. 0.1 M HCl
6. 0.1 M acetic acid (CH_3COOH)
7. 0.1 M sodium acetate ($CH_3COO^-Na^+$)
8. 0.1 M carbonic acid or club soda or seltzer
9. 0.1 M $NaHCO_3$
10. 0.1 M $NH_3(aq)$ (aqueous ammonia)
11. 0.1 M NaOH
12. Spot plate
13. 10-mL beakers

16 EXPERIMENT 16

Pre-Lab Questions

1. What is a Bronsted-Lowry acid? : What is a Bronsted-Lowry base?

2. Provide the formula of the conjugate base for each of the following acids:
   a. HCl

   b. H_2CO_3

   c. H_3PO_4

3. The pH of blood is 7.4 and that for saliva is 6.4. Which of the two is more basic?

16   EXPERIMENT 16

Report Sheet

pH of solutions	**1.** *by pH paper*	**2.** *by pH meter*
0.1 M HCl	_____	_____not done_____
0.1 M acetic acid	_____	_____
0.1 M sodium acetate	_____	_____
0.1 M carbonic acid	_____	_____
0.1 M sodium bicarbonate	_____	_____
0.1 M ammonia	_____	_____
0.1 M NaOH	_____	_____not done_____

Buffer system a   *pH*

3. 5 mL 0.1 M CH_3COOH + 5 mL 0.1 M $CH_3COO^-Na^+$ _____

4. after addition of 0.5 mL 0.1 M HCl   _____

5. after addition of 0.5 mL 0.1 M NaOH   _____

Buffer system b

6. 1 mL 0.1 M CH_3COOH + 10 mL 0.1 M $CH_3COO^-Na^+$ _____

7. after addition of 0.5 mL 0.1 M HCl   _____

8. after addition of 0.5 mL 0.1 M NaOH   _____

Buffer system c

9. 5 mL 0.1 M H_2CO_3 + 5 mL 0.1 M $NaHCO_3$ _____

10. after addition of 0.5 mL 0.1 M HCl   _____

11. after addition of 0.5 mL 0.1 M NaOH   _____

Buffer system d

12. 1 mL 0.1 M H_2CO_3 + 10 mL 0.1 M $NaHCO_3$ _____

13. after addition of 0.5 mL 0.1 M HCl   _____

14. after addition of 0.5 mL 0.1 M NaOH   _____

No buffer system

15. distilled water   _____

16. after addition of 0.5 mL 0.1 M HCl   _____

17. after addition of 0.5 mL 0.1 M NaOH   _____

Post-Lab Questions

1. Can distilled water be an effective buffer? Use data from your experiment to support your answer.

2. Calculate the expected pH values of the buffer systems from the experiments (a, b, c, d), using the Henderson-Hasselbalch equation, $pH = pKa + \log([A^-]/[HA])$. Use for pK_a values: carbonic acid = 6.37 and acetic acid = 4.75.

a.

b.

c.

d.

STANDARD ATOMIC WEIGHTS OF THE ELEMENTS 2007 Based on relative atomic mass of $^{12}C = 12$, where ^{12}C is a neutral atom in its nuclear and electronic ground state.[†]

Name	Symbol	Atomic Number	Atomic Weight	Name	Symbol	Atomic Number	Atomic Weight
Actinium*	Ac	89	(227)	Neodymium	Nd	60	144.242(3)
Aluminum	Al	13	26.9815386(2)	Neon	Ne	10	20.1797(6)
Americium*	Am	95	(243)	Neptunium*	Np	93	(237)
Antimony	Sb	51	121.760(1)	Nickel	Ni	28	58.6934(4)
Argon	Ar	18	39.948(1)	Niobium	Nb	41	92.90638(2)
Arsenic	As	33	74.92160(2)	Nitrogen	N	7	14.0067(2)
Astatine*	At	85	(210)	Nobelium*	No	102	(259)
Barium	Ba	56	137.327(7)	Osmium	Os	76	190.23(3)
Berkelium*	Bk	97	(247)	Oxygen	O	8	15.9994(3)
Beryllium	Be	4	9.012182(3)	Palladium	Pd	46	106.42(1)
Bismuth	Bi	83	208.98040(1)	Phosphorus	P	15	30.973763(2)
Bohrium	Bh	107	(272)	Platinum	Pt	78	195.084(9)
Boron	B	5	10.811(7)	Plutonium*	Pu	94	(244)
Bromine	Br	35	79.904(1)	Polonium*	Po	84	(209)
Cadmium	Cd	48	112.411(8)	Potassium	K	19	39.0983(1)
Cesium	Cs	55	132.9054519(2)	Praseodymium	Pr	59	140.90765(2)
Calcium	Ca	20	40.078(4)	Promethium*	Pm	61	(145)
Californium*	Cf	98	(251)	Protactinium*	Pa	91	231.03588(2)
Carbon	C	6	12.0107(8)	Radium*	Ra	88	(226)
Cerium	Ce	58	140.116(1)	Radon*	Rn	86	(222)
Chlorine	Cl	17	35.453(2)	Rhenium	Re	75	186.207(1)
Chromium	Cr	24	51.9961(6)	Rhodium	Rh	45	102.90550(2)
Cobalt	Co	27	58.933195(5)	Roentgenium	Rg	111	(280)
Copper	Cu	29	63.546(3)	Rubidium	Rb	37	85.4678(3)
Curium*	Cm	96	(247)	Ruthenium	Ru	44	101.07(2)
Darmstadtium	Ds	110	(281)	Rutherfordium	Rf	104	(267)
Dubnium	Db	105	(268)	Samarium	Sm	62	150.36(2)
Dysprosium	Dy	66	162.500(1)	Scandium	Sc	21	44.955912(6)
Einsteinium*	Es	99	(252)	Seaborgium	Sg	106	(271)
Erbium	Er	68	167.259(3)	Selenium	Se	34	78.96(3)
Europium	Eu	63	151.964(1)	Silicon	Si	14	28.0855(3)
Fermium*	Fm	100	(257)	Silver	Ag	47	107.8682(2)
Fluorine	F	9	18.9984032(5)	Sodium	Na	11	22.98976928(2)
Francium*	Fr	87	(223)	Strontium	Sr	38	87.62(1)
Gadolinium	Gd	64	157.25(3)	Sulfur	S	16	32.065(5)
Gallium	Ga	31	69.723(1)	Tantalum	Ta	73	180.94788(2)
Germanium	Ge	32	72.64(1)	Technetium*	Tc	43	(98)
Gold	Au	79	196.966569(4)	Tellurium	Te	52	127.60(3)
Hafnium	Hf	72	178.49(2)	Terbium	Tb	65	158.92535(2)
Hassium	Hs	108	(270)	Thallium	Tl	81	204.3833(2)
Helium	He	2	4.002602(2)	Thorium*	Th	90	232.03806(2)
Holmium	Ho	67	164.93032(2)	Thulium	Tm	69	168.93421(2)
Hydrogen	H	1	1.00794(7)	Tin	Sn	50	118.710(7)
Indium	In	49	114.818(3)	Titanium	Ti	22	47.867(1)
Iodine	I	53	126.90447(3)	Tungsten	W	74	183.84(1)
Iridium	Ir	77	192.217(3)	Ununbium	Uub	112	(285)
Iron	Fe	26	55.845(2)	Ununhexium	Uuh	116	(292)
Krypton	Kr	36	83.798(2)	Ununoctium	Uuo	118	(294)
Lanthanum	La	57	138.90547(7)	Ununpentium	Uup	115	(228)
Lawrencium*	Lr	103	(262)	Ununquadium	Uuq	114	(289)
Lead	Pb	82	207.2(1)	Ununtrium	Uut	113	(284)
Lithium	Li	3	6.941(2)	Uranium*	U	92	238.02891(3)
Lutetium	Lu	71	174.9668(1)	Vanadium	V	23	50.9415(1)
Magnesium	Mg	12	24.3050(6)	Xenon	Xe	54	131.293(6)
Manganese	Mn	25	54.938045(5)	Ytterbium	Yb	70	173.054(5)
Meitnerium	Mt	109	(276)	Yttrium	Y	39	88.90585(2)
Mendelevium*	Md	101	(258)	Zinc	Zn	30	65.38(2)
Mercury	Hg	80	200.59(2)	Zirconium	Zr	40	91.224(2)
Molybdenum	Mo	42	95.96(2)				

[†]The atomic weights of many elements can vary depending on the origin and treatment of the sample. This is particularly true for Li; commercially available lithium-containing materials have Li atomic weights in the range of 6.939 and 6.996. The uncertainties in atomic weight values are given in parentheses following the last significant figure to which they are attributed.

*Elements with no stable nuclide; the value given in parentheses is the atomic mass number of the isotope of longest known half-life. However, three such elements (Th, Pa, and U) have a characteristic terrestial isotopic composition, and the atomic weight is tabulated for these. http://www.chem.qmw.ac.uk/iupac/AtWt/